To Ginny—
　　Aloha—
　　　　Dick

June 17, 1937

LIFE & DEATH

Life & Death

THE AUTOBIOGRAPHY
OF A SURGEON

by

ANDREA MAJOCCHI

Translated by Wallace Brockway

New York
KNIGHT PUBLICATIONS
1937

CONTENTS

LIFE & DEATH

Chapter I

PROLOGUE

MY LIFE BEGAN TRAGICALLY.

My father died at the age of thirty-two, after a few days' illness, victim of an infection he had caught while performing an autopsy. After two years as a parish doctor, he had managed to scale the first rung of a ladder that would have carried him, had he lived, to a position of great distinction in the art and science of hygiene. He had earned a good post in the Central Hospital at Cremona, and this was to have been merely the beginning of the brilliant career predicted by his many admirers.

Everything seemed to smile on him: family, profession, scientific future. His sacrifices stood to be rewarded when a hideous professional accident snatched him away brutally, violently, from science, art, family.

As his illness rapidly progressed, my father foresaw its inevitable *dénouement*, and with feverish anxiety charged his wife with the care of the children. I was then three years old, my sister was two, and there was another child on the way—my brother—whom my father was not destined to see.

"Maria," he said brokenly, "I am dying. I commit our children to your care. Remember I would rather have them peasants than doctors."

These were the last words my father spoke before becoming delirious. My beloved mother (she was twenty-six years old, and five months pregnant) nursed him selflessly. He died within a few days.

A gray marble plaque, set in the wall of the vestibule of the Central Hospital at Cremona, still informs visitors that Dr. Giuseppe Majocchi died at the age of thirty-two, a martyr to medical science.

They buried him in the little cemetery of his native town, and over his grave many were the tears, many the regrets. For he was well liked, and his tragic end had moved his fellow villagers. Our relatives were generous enough in their promises—they were quite glib in assuring us poor children that, in losing one father, we had gained several. But the facts fell short of the words.

Of the mourners only one, during the years that followed, did much more than we had reason to hope, and he alone had not spoken in the hour of our greatest sorrow. My uncle Antonio had said nothing, simply because grief had left him speechless. My father had been more than a brother to him—he had almost been his child.

My father was the younger by a year, but they had lived together in the same *pension* at Lodi, at the same prep school, in the same academy (even in the same class). Although he was the younger, my father, with his keen mind, had made up a year in school. He was in many ways the typical precocious child, even in his many lively prejudices that only the more mature wisdom of the elder brother could curb. But he was, in any event, good and sincere, sympathetic with all, a favorite with the professors, and conspicuously successful in the examinations, even when he had not studied much.

Then they went together to the University at Pavia.

There they had shared the same room, had eaten at the same table. Only, Uncle Antonio had chosen mathematics, and my father, medicine. The choice of profession separated them, but could not touch their affection for each other.

And now the cherished companion of Uncle Antonio's youth and studies had been struck down by a hideous accident. His poor children could not be left to starve. . . . In the warm heart of the remaining brother an idea grew. He was betrothed to a younger sister of my mother. He would marry her at once, and take my mother and her brood into his home, educating his nephews and niece along with his own children.

The idea seemed worthy of the love he bore his dead brother, and he could scarcely wait to discuss it with his bride-to-be. But when the time came for him to confide his big idea, Uncle Antonio was overcome with emotion. His eyes filled with tears, and he could not speak. But Aunt Giulia understood at once, and threw her arms around his neck. There was no need to say any more.

For she had had the same idea: Maria would go to them at once, and would advise and help Giulia. And if children came, Maria could help to raise them. But right now, here were the poor orphans to be considered, and they would be brought up together, with two mothers to guide them.

They decided to tell my mother of their decision.

It is not exaggerating to call my mother's condition, at that time, desperate. She had borne two children during her four years of married life, and now came my father's tragic death, with the financial difficulties that inevitably followed. As if this were not enough to bear, with my father so recently buried, she had to put up with petty bickerings with relatives, envy, annoyance. Worst of all, she was five months pregnant.

But her first consideration was for her children. How could she raise the poor little things? Where could she find the material means and the moral stamina to launch them fairly in life? Under such psychological conditions, my uncle's proposal was a godsend, and it was accepted with enthusiasm. The two families were united.

All was not roses, but neither was it all thorns.

A modest seven-room apartment was our first home in Milan: the second floor of the house at 7, Via Crocefisso. Whenever I am in that neighborhood, I never neglect to glance sentimentally at the humble scene of my early childhood. I passed, in that house, from childish unconsciousness to my first callow impressions of life. Then begin my memories; for I have only the haziest impression of anything that came before. And those earliest memories return to haunt me with an ineffable sweetness, now that more than fifty years have gone by.

The most beloved figure that emerges from the atmosphere of these years is, of course, my mamma. How lovely she seemed to me! There was no woman her equal in the whole world. And how clever she was! How finely she sang, for example! When she was rocking my little brother to sleep, she often sang a famous aria by Rossini or Verdi. Then I crept stealthily into the darkened room, and hid myself behind the door in an ecstasy of listening. When she had finished, I ran out and kissed her hand.

My mother had an exquisite appreciation of the arts, as well as a phenomenal memory. While she was busy in the kitchen (for cooking was one of her tasks), she was wont to recite softly whole cantos of Dante or Tasso and the poems of Foscolo, Leopardi, and Parini. I stood by, listening open-mouthed and making my first acquaintance of Farinata degli Uberti and Godfrey of Bouillon.

But what delighted me most was to sit on a stool at my mother's feet while she was cooking. Then she would tell me many fine stories, and if I failed to understand anything, I begged her to explain, even asking strange questions about the weird ideas that crowded my brain.

"Mamma dear, why are we born?"

"Because God created us."

"Why did He do that?"

"To know Him, to love Him, and to serve Him in this life, that we may enjoy Him elsewhere."

"Why," I asked dubiously, "can we not enjoy Him in this world?"

My mother kissed me, and said sadly, "My poor child, happiness does not exist in this world."

I looked into her eyes and knew that she must be very sad, my poor mamma, because Papa had gone away forever, and she was alone. But I—I thought suddenly—would be her companion, to console and cheer her with my constant solicitude. I felt this was my duty, that I should do it at all costs, and that it must define the scope of my life.

Meanwhile, as time passed, the double family changed. Aunt Giulia had her first child—a daughter, Giacinta. This was very jolly for everyone, especially Uncle Antonio, who was even more pleased the following year when a boy, Achille, was born. Then came another boy, Carlo, when, to tell the truth, joy was a bit restrained.

After Carlo (always with a year between them) came

Pia, then Maria, then Giuseppina, then Emilio, and, finally, Gigi. . . . My aunt despaired, for each pregnancy was accompanied, at first, by neurasthenia and acute suffering. My uncle opened his eyes wider and wider . . . and said nothing. Silently he strove to increase his income: he rose with the sun and hurried to his office. In the evening he brought home his huge ledgers, and often worked on them until the small hours. Sometimes I watched him while he wrote silently: I felt strangely disturbed, tender and yet heartbroken.

There were now ten children in the family, and we had to move from the little apartment in the Via Crocefisso to a larger one in the Via San Bernardo, at No. 16, right behind the Central Hospital.

I was the first of the brood, and so I was, in a larger sense, its real leader. I considered study a pastime, and before I was fifteen years old, I finished preparatory school. My teachers encouraged me in those hopes which are so agreeable to the youthful imagination.

My poor mamma was only too proud of me, but, alas! how could I pursue my studies with the scanty means at my disposal? My good uncle, already weighed down with so many responsibilities, could not assume another. My other relatives were generous enough with their fine words of encouragement, and even with small gifts—but that was all. I thought I might compete for a scholarship from the Congregazione di Carità, and I did so, successfully. This meant only a few hundred liras a year, but it sufficed to lighten the worse drains on the meager household budget.

Without that little scholarship I could not have gone on with my studies.

My mother interpreted this unlooked-for aid as a sign of

God's personal intervention: it rewarded her sacrifices, compensated her for the hardships she had endured. Now I would be able to go to the academy, and then—well, Providence would find the way again. For my mother believed in a Providence that had sustained her throughout, giving her the strength to resist despair.

Poor Mamma! When I think of her spirit of sacrifice, of her strength of mind, and of her self-denial, my memories engender an emotion that is both sweet and sad. For she was young and lovely, talented and cultured, and eminently fitted for a spacious and contented life. Instead, she lived only for her children: she devoted herself to our interests.

We looked on her as a living manifestation of goodness; she was our guide and our salvation. Even today, after all the years that she has been dead, gray-haired and experienced as I am, I remember her advice and her faith, careful to lead the kind of life she showed me. Often, in the difficulties and cares of life, during sleepless nights, when I feel the need of courage to grapple with the grave problems confronting me, when I am afraid of losing my way in the labyrinth of doubts, and know not what decision to make, just when I am most depressed the sole and constant appeal springs most naturally and spontaneously to my lips: "Mamma!"

The exemption from tuition fees and the scholarship money had allowed me to enter the academy.

How proud I felt as an academy boy! And how much grander than my brother and sister and my cousins! I can truly say that my desire for—and joy in—learning were greater than any mere vanity I felt in my new status. To me, the academy symbolized my passage from childhood to intellectual maturity.

Naturally, not all the studies pleased me equally. Mathematics, for example, could scarcely be called a passion of mine. Not that I did not recognize its beauty and importance, but it demanded concentration and kept me in a nervous strain that did not suit my restless spirit.

I followed the courses in classical literature with satisfaction. Among the sciences, physics pleased me the most, but wearied me a bit when I passed from the simple observation of phenomena to calculations based on strictly mathematical formulae. I also had a taste for chemistry, and all the so-called natural sciences interested me: above all, I delighted in learning the structure of the human body and the functions of the various organs. It seemed to me that the human organism was nature's masterpiece, and that, by studying and understanding the various organs, their functions, and their interrelationships, man really attained self-knowledge—an understanding of that *Nosce te ipsum* which is the root of all wisdom.

But what attracted me the most—this may seem a strange confession in these times—was philosophy. I had the good fortune to have Angelo Brofferio as a teacher—a truly great master who is today, unhappily, almost forgotten. I can still remember, with surprising vividness, the eagerness with which I followed his arguments, and the discussions I attempted with him, especially when we skirted such lofty matters as free will, the immortality of the soul, and God.

My school friends sometimes laughed at me, and mockingly reproached me for ascending to the clouds, assuring me also that a philosopher would never make his mark in the world. Practically speaking, they might be right, but

my impression of those years convinces me that proneness
to philosophical speculations had helped to shape my mental attitudes and to fix firmly in my psyche those convictions and principles which have never changed throughout
my life.

My studies took up the greater part of my time, but not
all. The leisure hours I dedicated to some minor passion—
and, above all, to music and foreign languages.

Music was, and always has been, the art I prefer. Even
as a baby, when I heard my mother sing the arias of Verdi
and Rossini, I went into ecstasies; but my joy was at its
height when, during vacations in the country, I could sit
at the organ during Mass.

The village schoolmaster functioned as organist: a most
intelligent man who would have gone far, had he been
born in other circumstances, but who, in the isolation of
Villavesco, a tiny village in the Bassa Lodigiana, had to
put up with everything in order to live and to steel himself
to the chore of bringing up, somehow, his ten or twelve
children. One of the posts he filled most willingly was that
of organist in the parish church, and he discharged his
duties with an efficiency and courage that compensated
for his lack of musical culture.

I remember him improvising, on the organ keyboard, the
sweetest melodies to accompany the religious ceremonies.
When the Host was elevated, he was accustomed to play
the *"Casta Diva"* from *Nórma* on the *vox humana*, and the
music seemed so sublime and so apt to my boyish heart
that Paradise alone (so I thought) could hold its equal.
When Mass was over and the people began to stream from
the lofty nave towards the church doors, he opened all
the stops for a final explosion of glory scored to the march

from *Aïda* or from *Jeanne d'Arc*, and then the church trembled with jubilation and joy, from the crypt to the top of the echoing nave.

It was a veritable manifestation of God—a magic that penetrated to the most secret recesses of my being, with an infinite sweetness. I descended from the choir loft in a trance, and thoughtlessly followed the good man to his house, begging him to tell me when he would be practicing his piano-playing so that I could continue my hero-worship.

I have said *piano*, but actually he used a wretched spinet which vibrated horribly whenever my friend launched enthusiastically into one of his favorite scores. Then myriads of notes crowded the little room, and escaped through the quiet lanes of the village.

One day, when my admiration had been more pronounced than ever, he turned to me with tears in his eyes, and said: "See here, Andreino"—I could not have been more than ten or eleven at the time—"you are a fine lad—a sensitive one, too. Remember that music ennobles the mind: do not neglect it in your education. I am going to speak to your mamma, and persuade her to let you take piano lessons."

And so he did, but my poor mother replied that there wasn't enough money for necessities. Why think of the luxuries? She was stubborn at times, that dear mamma of mine, but I was more stubborn than she. I recalled a certain savings-bank book with ninety-five liras*—little presents from my grandmother and other relatives—to my credit. Mamma had the book, but the money was mine; she had to give it to me, and let me buy a piano.

* The lira is worth approximately twenty cents in American currency.

A piano with ninety-five liras? Of course, it seems absurd today, but nevertheless I had seen a sign, over a door in the Via Campo Lodigiano, advertising an upright piano for sale at a hundred liras. I needed five more, but I did not give up hope of wheedling them out of somebody. And so, one fine winter afternoon, the movers installed the disgraceful-looking instrument in my bedroom.

Uncle Antonio and Aunt Giulia exchanged an expressive look, and then burst out in laughter so scornful, and long-drawn-out, and Olympian, that I was almost struck dumb with mortification. They insisted on referring to my poor old piano as "that wooden dromedary."

But three months later, when I showed what I could do with scales and arpeggios, they did not laugh at all. Thanks to a kind lady of our acquaintance, I was soon deep in Czerny and the sonatinas of Clementi; a year later I ventured to try the Beethoven bagatelles and Mozart's sonatas. And later on, and for many years, my noisy "dromedary" was my most faithful friend: the beloved instrument to which I confided my joys and my sorrows, my enthusiasms and my dreams.

Only much later, after I had passed my examinations, did my first real earnings allow me to retire my old friend, substituting a fine concert grand piano, which is today the most cherished object in my music room.

Besides music, I had a weakness for foreign languages. The preparatory schools and academies were then completely lacking in such instructions; so I had to work on my own hook.

Why I had such a precocious passion for the foreign languages is beyond me. Possibly I thought them a kind of liberation from the definite limits of our culture and traditional life, and as I wanted to know the world, to travel, to go to far-off places, they seemed the first requisites to fulfilling my desires.

It is true that though the knowledge of foreign languages was of great use to me in my medical studies and in my profession, I could not have foreseen that. Language study, at first, was just good sport.

I began with the study of English. Fortunately I had met, among the family friends, an old missionary returned from the United States—a worthy priest who had spent long years in parochial work in Nashville, Tennessee, where he had performed miracles of goodness, energy, and charity. He had gone to this distant place when only the barest rudiments of civilization existed there, and had witnessed, and had even largely promoted, a development in local conditions that was truly phenomenal.

So he loved America as one loves the scenes and companions of his youth; returned to Milan for reasons of age and health, he continued to read English books and newspapers. Teaching this language was, to him, like renewing his youth, and even like doing a bit of propaganda.

The kindly old man suggested that he give me lessons (free ones, he meant); I accepted enthusiastically, and just as eagerly set to work during the hours not devoted to academic preparation. In a short time, I possessed a working knowledge of the English language.

My courage was so overweening that I decided myself to give lessons in English (shameless fellow that I was!), and I recall that my first pupil was a good friend who had just returned from Germany, where he had gone to study weaving. Having a perfect knowledge of German, he had expressed the desire to learn English. "Very well," I said solemnly, "I will teach you English, and you will teach me German."

And so it was, with the sole difference that I learned German at a magnificent rate, and poor Silvio did not learn English at all. Was it the teacher's fault, or the pupil's? I cannot say, but I am sure that after a few months it developed that he could easily live without English, while my longing for German grew apace. Already I began to plan for a tour of Germany.

Germany! It was a magic word in those days, for then it was true that whatever anyone considered excellent came from Germany: science, books, music, industrial arts and devices, and even literature. The theaters played only Wagner, and the concert halls only Beethoven, Schubert, Mendelssohn, Brahms, etc. In the sciences the Germans ruled supreme, and so too was the case in industry.

Germany was looked on as a victorious and happy country whose superiority was indisputable. But where could I dig up the funds for the two months' vacation needed to perfect my German? I had only to continue giving English lessons (news of my proficiency had got around), and so I did. I recall that during these crucial times I had an almost illustrious pupil, the cashier of the savings bank, who had a passion for the natural sciences, and wanted, at all costs, to read Darwin in the original.

So at the end of a year I succeeded in accumulating three hundred liras (quite a sum, believe me), and that seemed enough to turn my dream into a reality. I spoke of my plans to my mamma, who listened downheartedly, and still more downheartedly packed my valise, and kissed me good-by with tears streaming down her face. One

would have thought I was going to the Far East, instead
of merely to Munich, in Bavaria, but it was the first time
I was going into the world alone.

When I think back to that first trip, I seem to relive
those ecstatically happy days of my youth. Twenty years
old, one small valise, and three hundred liras. I was happy,
and meant to stay away until every bit of my money was
gone.

How delightful the view from the moving train seemed
to me! The Tyrol, through which I passed on the way to
the Bavarian frontier, was fine country. And the train was
as comfortable as could be.

I alighted at the Central Station in Munich, and was immediately accosted by a lady who asked me, *"Sind Sie
Italiener?"*

Struck dumb by such insight, I nodded my head, and
was about to ask how she knew my nationality. But she
did not give me time, and, without further ado, offered
me room and board at her house, all for ninety liras a
month. As far as price was concerned, I could not wish for
any better terms, so I accepted. The good lady escorted
me to the Pension Concordia, Luitpoldstrasse 10. On the
way, she told me that her name was Frau Fenzl, and that
she had lodged several Italians who had been very pleased
with her house. Her clientele, she said, was a very good
one.

The Pension Concordia turned out to be a clean, handsome house. My room was almost magnificent, and the
dining room was quite splendid: there they served only
the *Mittagessen*—we ate the *Abendessen* in the kitchen, a
vast flagstoned chamber with plastered walls that shone
like mirrors.

In due time I met Anna, the beauteous housemaid, and during the meal the other guests of the Concordia. I blessed my German lessons, for no one understood Italian. There was a Fräulein Horowitz, the manager of a fashion shop, and an agreeable chatterbox of a woman. Fräulein Renier (an assumed name—I never knew her real one) acted at the Deutsches Theater, and though not pretty, was well informed. Besides Herr Scholtz, who owned a large flower-shop in the Karlsplatz, there were several young business-men. There were no students, possibly because it was the time of the school vacations.

The company was pleasant, and, indeed, seemed posi-tively delightful, because all chattered so willingly, and I wanted nothing better than to chatter myself as much as possible—for the sake of my German. I had systematized my day so well that it was agreed that I would begin by escorting Fräulein Horowitz to her fashion shop. Then I would return to pick up Fräulein Renier, walk with her to the Deutsches Theater for the rehearsals, and finally wind up at my friend Scholtz' flowershop in the Karlsplatz, where I would loiter talking to the clerks.

Every Sunday all the Concordians went for an excursion into the country. Delightful walks along the banks of the Isar, in the park of Nymphenburg, on the shores of the Starnbergersee. If the company was most sympathetic, the places themselves seemed even more lovely, and Munich, with its wide streets, gardens, and museums, a veritable paradise.

The sin was that this delectable existence could not last. Before the end of the second month my three hundred liras were exhausted, and only my return ticket remained.

So I made up a story about family matters . . . and announced my departure.

There was an explosion of regret: everyone liked me. They had dubbed me *das Kind der Pension*, because I was the youngest, and each in his own way had taken me under his wing. They gave me a farewell evening at the Münchener Café, then embraced me, with tears in their eyes, and made me promise to return.

Yes, I surely would return, for that month and a half had been so full of happiness, Germany so fine and progressive, Munich so neat and lovely, all art and gentleness. With my eyes brimming over with tears, I bade farewell to the pinnacles of the cathedral and to the cupola of the church of the Theatines, and swore I would return as soon as I had earned my first money.

In fact, I returned thirteen years later. What a mistake!

In 1909 I left Berlin, after finishing my thesis *Libera Docenza*, and, bound for Italy, I recalled my youthful vow. So I chose the route over the Brenner so that I could stop three days in Munich. My heart beat when I alighted at that same Central Station, and I burned with desire to see my lovely city, my gay *pension*, possibly my old friends.

I set out from the station to the Luitpoldstrasse.

The city did not seem as lovely, as neat, as lively as before. (Was it because I had come from Berlin?) I hurried to the Pension Concordia. But, was this the house I had admired so much? It had seemed less humble, even neater. Was this really the stair, this the door?

I rang, and Frau Fenzl herself came to open the door. But how old and ugly she was!

She did not recognize me. When I told her my name, she found me much changed. *"Ach! Herr Majocchi, das Kind der Pension!"*

And the others? Fräulein Horowitz, Fräulein Renier, Scholtz, Anna—all my old friends? Were none of them still there?

Alas, not one!

The Horowitz had gone to Vienna, where she had died. The Renier, after serious professional disappointments, had retired, she knew not where. Scholtz, after business reverses, had wound up his business, and retired to the Riviera for his health. Even the prosperous Anna had ended badly.

Of the others Frau Fenzl knew nothing.

I glanced at my little room, the dining room, the kitchen. . . . It is absolutely true that the appearance of the outward world is colored as the color of our own life changes.

I walked slowly into the street. My throat was parched, and I walked back mechanically to the Central Station. I took the first train for Italy, and when once again I saw the pinnacles of the cathedral and the cupola of the church of the Theatines disappear, a sigh rose from my heart—a sigh that was almost a sob.

It would have been better if I had not gone back.

"O mein altes Heidelberg!"

Farewell to youth.

Chapter II

FAREWELL TO YOUTH

> Hang there like fruit, my soul,
> Till the tree dies.
> —Tennyson

MUCH TO MY JOY, I SECURED MY ACADEMY SHEEPSKIN without having to take examinations. But the pleasure yielded to the immediate need of choosing a career.

This is a serious decision for a young man—perhaps the most serious in his entire life.

I was in a quandary. I didn't like mathematics, which would have brought me a degree in engineering. Law was a career for rich gentlemen, not for a poor fellow like myself. There remained letters or medicine. My mother secretly leaned to the former: she told me that I had a knack of teaching, and besides, she had a holy terror of medicine, which recalled my father's tragic death and his advice on his deathbed. My uncle, however, was all for medicine. It meant six long years at the University, true, but I still had that scholarship purse of mine tucked away.

"Furthermore," Uncle Antonio argued, "it is the one career that bears fruit at once. You will be sure to get an official post." The idea was not especially pleasing, but it was better than dying of hunger. The practical arguments of my uncle won the day: I decided for medicine.

I matriculated at Pavia in November.

At last I was a university student: a *goliardo**. Yet I must admit that I expected something much finer from my new status.

My first impressions of the university left me disillusioned. Neither university nor town measured up to the splendid conception I had formed of them in my youthfully sanguine mind: the austerity of the scientific discipline, the great traditions, the promise of a triumphant future. I can almost say that neither the school, nor the instruction, nor the students satisfied me. Nothing convinced me.

The University of Pavia had fallen upon evil days: dirty, dilapidated premises, a limited number of courses, lack of apparatus. Besides, other details wounded my sensibilities. That nasty old anatomy theater, for example, with its filthy benches covered with obscene inscriptions and pornographic drawings: the heritage from countless generations of students.

And those filthy couplets that they sang before class, with complete indifference to the women students. Other things even worse. . . . If this was college spirit, it was no credit to those who had been greeted and complimented, in the academic speeches, as the flower of the coming generations. Even the studies themselves filled me with astonishment. Certain courses, such as botany, physics, zoology, chemistry, were little more than mere repetitions of what I had learned at the academy; others were taught so carelessly and were interrupted by so many absences that one felt that the professors felt less enthusiasm than the students.

* A student of a medieval university. Pavia, one of the oldest universities in the world, was founded in the fourteenth century.—TRANSLATOR.

I have a vivid memory of my first anatomy lesson, and how astonished I was to see the sort of anatomical specimens they showed us. For instance, there was a young woman's leg that was brought into the theater the first time I showed up for a practical demonstration; it was very well modeled, waxlike, and remarkably malodorous, but whether more from corpse or formaldehyde I cannot say.

I was unable to eat meat for a fortnight: every time I sat down for a meal this macabre vision would rise up before my eyes; every time I took a bite of food I suffered as though I were obliged to eat corpses. Evidently others, if not all, felt the same. Some had even slily decided to change their careers, and had matriculated in other courses.

I resisted the temptation.

Fortunately so, for at the end of my third year things became better. This third year was of exceptional importance: it was devoted to anatomy, physiology, and general pathology—the very essence of the instruction: the granite columns on which the entire medical edifice rests.

No one can cure an illness without understanding the sick organ, without knowing how it functions, and without having the fundamental knowledge of morbose processes. It is impossible to get along without these three fundamental courses, and it is truly painful to see how easily students today are permitted to evade these three examinations.

As for myself, I had understood their importance, and had devoted all my energies to such studies. The third year at the University was hard work, but when at the end I passed the stiff anatomy examination with flying

colors, I felt that I had already gone far on the road that I
intended to follow.

I was well grounded in the essentials of a difficult profession, and this solid preparation was of major importance
during my career.

At the beginning of my fourth year began the practical
part of my medical studies. I had free access to the clinics,
I was admitted to the hospitals.

The sick person is to the physician what the altar is
to the priest: he represents the object of all his cares. It
is no longer a question of abstract scientific curiosity, but
a practical one of a prompt cure, with the aid of all intellectual and moral faculties.

Only when confronted with actual sickness does the
medical student understand the loftiness of his mission;
only at the sickbed, whether in hospital or clinic, can he
realize the beauty and gravity of his task.

When I entered a clinic I felt as though I were entering
a temple, a holy place. But among the university clinics
that which impressed me most was the surgical one, pre-
sided over, in my time, by a truly great man: Enrico
Bottini.

He held his classes in a spacious amphitheater of the
old hospital of San Matteo—an amphitheater which then
represented everything that was majestic and imposing.
His lessons were attended not only by the students but by
faculty members who came to admire the almost legendary
figure who had the fame of a magician—a sublime operator. So the benches were always crowded, and the master's
coming was awaited impatiently.

The silence was especially imposing when, on the stroke

of the hour sounded by the school clock, the doors of the operating theater were flung wide, and Professor Bottini entered with all his suite. An emperor could not have advanced with more majesty; there was in his carriage something of the wrestler as well as of the teacher. He was a robust old gentleman, with a lion's head, an eagle eye, and a stubborn, square chin. There was something theatrical in his gestures (whether affected or natural I cannot say) which won his audience. In no other school were the students so well disciplined: before this magician alone did they feel like pygmies and hang on his every word. It seemed that all were thinking the same thing: *Quis ut deus?* And the god began his lecture over the poor patient, who was shriveled up under the white bedclothing of his little hospital cot until he almost disappeared.

The surgical lectures were often interspersed with the most caustic satire. The master's discourse was full of wit. With a mordant dialectic, an incredible finesse, the great man attacked all those he wished to rally or to punish: sick person or student, assistants and aides, colleagues far and wide—all felt the lash of his sarcastic tongue. The hour seemed to fly.

After the lesson came the operations in the same amphitheater. The entourage withdrew temporarily for the necessary disinfection, while the hospital assistants prepared the patient and gave the anesthetic.

After a quarter of an hour the operator and his suite come back, this time in battle array. White uniforms, white linen, steel instruments, an atmosphere of disinfectants and narcotics. The audience lean forward in the crowded galleries—there is a decided tension in the air, and some grow pale . . . they even creep from their places and disappear. But these are the novices.

The magician is there, imposing and sure of himself. He is the master of the situation. With knife in hand he seems to be waiting for the right moment. At last the narcotic takes effect, and the flesh is cut: the blood spurts out, but the operator is unmoved. His hands move rapidly, almost with the ability of a sleight-of-hand artist, and seem to be mixed up with those of his assistants. However (to cite the master's own words), the distance between them is astronomical.

In the twinkling of an eye, the tumor is found and extracted; the hole is closed, the tissues are stitched in place: the operation is over.

A sigh of relief from the crowded galleries—and then, a prolonged symphony of applause. This was what Bottini prized the most, this approval of the pupils for the master: it was the ovation given to the triumphant gladiator.

Oh, if I too could rise to those heights! If I too could draw such an audience to hang on my every word, and could operate so perfectly!

He seemed legendary to me, superhuman, almost divine. He who did all this was more than a man—he was a hero. I left the amphitheater, staggering and in a dream, with the master's words ringing in my head:

Surgery, science and art divine.

Less theatrical, but younger; less brilliant, but more cultured, there shone, in the university skies at the time, another star whom I admired profoundly.

He was Luigi Mangiagalli.

His clinic was located on the other side of the same

building, and was devoted to obstetrical and gynecological cases, constituting one of the most important branches of surgery. Mangiagalli, however, extended the confines of his speciality so as to include almost all medical knowledge within his province.

The classes were held in a fine amphitheater equal in shape and size to Bottini's though he did not operate there. Mangiagalli's more modern methods insisted on a separate place where operations could be performed with a complete guarantee against sepsis. Students who wished to view his operations had to submit to the most careful disinfection, and had to enter one by one.

The clinical lectures of Mangiagalli were truly magnificent. They were not rich in oratorical adornments: the diction was simple, but the exposition of his meaning was precise and comprehensive. Not one word outside the strictly medical consideration, no brilliant digressions—but scientific conciseness and absolute clarity. The eloquence developed by this method was ordered and logical; it was impossible to be drawn away or to wander: one had to follow this exacting speaker, who compelled the listeners' attention, and pitilessly held it to the end. Mangiagalli's culture and diverse knowledge were as amazing as his subtle and penetrating logic.

Bottini was the thaumaturge (I almost said the sleight-of-hand artist) of the surgical art, while Mangiagalli was its most profound and cultivated clinician, the exact logician, the incomparable teacher. Further, the first was the setting sun, the second a star in the ascendant.

In his *Giovinezza di Giulio Cesare*, Rovani tells how the dictator answered the friends of Pompey that man naturally worships the rising rather than the setting sun. It is not surprising, then, that I felt more drawn to Mangiagalli, and that I favored the branch of surgery that he taught and not general surgery, to which I had thought myself dedicated. I asked to assist him as interne in the course of my fifth year, and from then on my life was given over entirely to study.

My devotion to the Istituto was such that I almost lived a hermit's life. Therefore my mother decided to move her little family to Pavia, so that she could see me from time to time.

In other ways my sacrifices were rewarded.

The obstetrical-gynecological clinic at Pavia had, under the direction of Mangiagalli, reached an indisputable superiority. Whatever was most modern in medical technique was sure to be found in that Istituto; there was not a scientific discovery or novelty that was not tried out there, whether in the research laboratory, or in the diagnostic clinic, or in the operating theater.

To get these results Mangiagalli had surrounded himself with collaborators and aides of the first order. It was a real school of giants: a picked collection of geniuses, each of individual worth. The fame of the school would still be great today, if death had not taken so many of its members.

Though few remain today of that distinguished group, they are among the foremost gynecologists in Italy: Clivio, director of the Genoa clinic; Ferroni, professor at Florence; Alfieri, at Milan; Bertino, at Padua. . . . The greatest of all, Resinelli, died after winning the chair at Florence, and Tridondani, that at Cagliari. Poor Costa, my cherished friend and companion, died early in life after getting his first appointment, at the Maternity Hospital, at Novara.

These were the men I found at Mangiagalli's side during my interneship at the Pavia clinic; these were the talents

I admired and copied, who pointed out the ideal way, and of whom I might have repeated, with Goethe:

Dahin, dahin!
Möcht' ich mit dir, o mein Geliebter, ziehn.

My six years of study were over, the examinations were passed, and my life as a student was over. I had finished my thesis on tubal pregnancy, and only the last formalities remained.

My comrades were deep in their work and fearful of the outcome. No longer were they the thoughtless, fun-loving boys of a few years before. Each revealed the man, even the physician of suffering humanity.

What awaited us? Work, of course, cares, fatigue. From among us would come the great doctors, who would seek the heights like eagles; many would remain on the ground, not less useful there, possibly, and perhaps closer to human suffering. But why linger over these unhappy thoughts? Until that moment we had been equals, and should gather round the same table, just as gay and noisy as we had ever been in the old anatomical theater.

Such was our last meal together. One warm evening in June, we gathered under the shade of the arbor of San Lanfranco, on the banks of the Ticino. It was a happy idea, for the old tavern of San Lanfranco was a sort of shrine for the students of Pavia.

There, on the highest point of the course of the Ticino, we commanded the whole length of the river. It was the goal of all our boating expeditions, our romantic walks through the green and silent woodland, which called up the fondest memories for all of us. In the springtime the tavern was buried under the white blossoms of the acacia, the blue of the wisteria, the red roses, and the blue irises, which diffused, all together, an enervating wave of perfume.

There, among the flowers and under the arbor, our farewell dinner took place.

We had put on festal attire, as the occasion was an important one; but at first joy scarcely showed its head. We needed a few glasses of the good wine of Casteggio and of Broni before we could turn into the bold young fellows of former times. When Casnigo had made his farewell address, after the witty and amusing toasts, there was an explosion of joy and tenderness.

Yes, we loved each other deeply, and we would always remain close friends. We even decided on a reunion every five years and, for our silver jubilee, twenty-five years later, to return, all of us, to the arbor of San Lanfranco, heavy with flowers and perfume, in the shade of those green groves, and surrounded by gurgling, whispering brooks, witnesses of the frolics of our youth.

How lovely life was then!

And we really did have our reunion, twenty-five years later, under the arbor of San Lanfranco, the same June day, a day radiant with warmth and sunlight. The scene had not changed, the flowers seemed the same as before in the perfumed spring air. In order better to evoke old memories, we arrived at the meeting place by following the stream in a flotilla of boats appropriately decorated for the occasion. But if the country inn had not changed, how changed, alas, were the men!

And how many were missing at the rendezvous!

Of the seventy of old, only forty-five showed up; some

had not been able to come at the last moment, but twenty were dead. Among them were some who had attained fame and gave promise of even greater things. The good Negri had died after discovering the microbe of rabies. Also missing was Moreschi, so well known for his inspired work in complement deviation. Another had died in line of duty, another had been killed in the World War. In short, when we began counting heads at the inn, there were plenty of long faces among those who had resolved to be gay at all costs. To lose twenty comrades in twenty-five years—it was too much. And we no longer recognized each other. We had gone away full of youth, and we found ourselves mature men, and more than mature. Some were unrecognizable because their formerly black hair had turned gray or white; others were bald, bent over, wrinkled: hard work, the struggle to earn a livelihood, professional disappointments—all had marked the comrades of my youth.

But fate had put impassable barriers between some of us. We had left as comrades and equals, and when we returned, we scarcely recognized one another. Rustic, sunburnt, clumsily dressed in their provincial or old-fashioned Sunday best, some of them seemed like real countrymen. One had only a poor practice as a country doctor or, even worse, another had been buried alive in some mountain hamlet, with only the druggist and the priest to bear him company, and compensate him for so many hardships.

They had descended from their retreats for this grand occasion, in order to see the companions of their youth. And they saw them; rather, they looked at them as if they were dreaming. "How old he has become! . . . How serious *that* fellow has become—he used to be so light! Look at how elegant Pasini now is. Why not? He's a professor at the University of Milan! God knows, he's earned it. Why, even Besta has gone up in the world—a professor of psychiatry! . . ."

They mournfully discuss the varying fortunes of all these who were equals as students. Some have acquired professorial gravity and the dignity of the professional accustomed to move in rich and distinguished society; they have the genial appearance that is one of the stigmata of a spacious life and large earnings. Others are broken-down and discouraged. . . .

Well, well, it is time to sit down for the banquet. Each chooses as his neighbor his best friend of the early years, and again the generous wine of Casteggio and of Broni serves to loosen the tongue and rejoice the heart. There are so many things to tell, so many things to confide.

Most of them are married; their children are grown up; some are already university students. "Oh, these blessed children, how pretentious and extravagant they are! They are not content with the modest life we led—they never have enough. We were plenty pleased with a ramble in the hills of Casteggio, a boating excursion, or a game of bowls —at the most, a ride on a bicycle. But they speak only of tennis, skiing, automobiles. They never have enough money —never! Yet they grow up sturdy and strong; their lives are more hygienic than ours: they don't drink the way their fathers did at the Three Lilies or the Golden Lion."

But what a hubbub! What is happening?

Oh, yes, the worthy Casnigo has arisen and, amid laughter and hurrahs, has once again delivered, with imperturbable gravity, the most comic of speeches. This time he even distributes commemorative medals: silver for all except the

four or five who have secured the highest scholastic grades
. . . and they get gold.

With the champagne, the gaiety reaches its height. We
have almost become students once again.

Finally the speaker invites us to another reunion five
years hence, and woe be to him who doesn't show up. . . .

The thirtieth anniversary came around, but the reunion
did not take place. At the time set for its celebration,
Casnigo, the beloved friend, the comrade of the university
days, the gay buffoon who had himself invited us to the
traditional festivity, as if to the celebration of a sacred rite,
lay on his deathbed.

A severe fever had struck him down, and, after two
months of acute pain and weakness, he succumbed.

I beheld that beloved face, formerly always so cheery
and now already cold in the awful rigidity of death, for
the last time: I followed the mortal remains to the grave,
and when the coffin was lowered into the ground, I felt
that every trace of youth had vanished from my life—that
every memory of this happy time had disappeared forever.

From that day to this no one has ever thought of another
reunion of the companions of former days . . . and perhaps they will never again be reunited.

Chapter III

THE STRUGGLE FOR EXISTENCE

Never give up, it is wiser and better
Always to hope than once to despair!
—Tupper: *Ballads and Poems*

HAPPY THE STUDENT WHO RETURNS WITH HIS DIPLOMAS
into the bosom of a wealthy family. The verses of Leopardi apply to him:

> *o giorni*
> *Vezzosi, inenarrabili; allor quando*
> *Al rapito mortal primieramente*
> *Sorridon le donzelle: a gara intorno*
> *Ogni cosa sorride: invidia tace*
> *Non desta ancora, ovver benigna: e quasi*
> *(Inusitata meraviglia) il mondo*
> *La destra soccorrevole gli porge!*

So the new doctor returns triumphant to his paternal
Lares.

He is no longer a student. He is a real doctor. In the
name of the king they have given him the diploma *in
utroque*, in medicine as well as in surgery. The mother
throws her arms around his neck, and looks at him proudly
through her tears; she kisses him—it is a respectful kiss, to
be sure, but it rings out triumphantly; then she presents
him with a gold watch, set in brilliants and engraved with

33

his monogram. The brothers and sisters look at him admiringly, enviously, almost with worship. The father greets him with shining eyes, and says, "Bravo!" Nothing more: emotion does not allow him to continue. He merely hands him a thick wallet crammed with new banknotes.

Then his mother has new visiting cards printed, and sends them to all her friends. She, the poor woman, can scarcely sit still. She wants to show off her happiness, for she is brimming over with it.

"Oh, my dear doctor," she purrs to her friends, "if you could see how serious he has become. What a brave boy he must be! Who knows where he may go? Just watch his career . . . !"

All want to know her dear doctor. They particularly want to see him, to rejoice with him, to admire him. And this desire extends to acquaintances far and wide; other charming mothers, accompanied by their daughters, come to visit his mamma, bursting with compliments and sizing up the handsome . . . I mean, the good young doctor with such a fine future ahead of him.

The mother is gurgling with joy; she approves of her good doctor, and recommends him to everybody. It is publicity that counts; in short, she wants to launch him. And the clientele is ready. The young doctor (incredible, isn't it?) has patients right away, particularly women. But the father does not care for these goings-on. His little son is not in want: he doesn't have to take the first thing that offers. No. He must be a specialist.

But a specialist in what? No one knows, but what does it matter? A specialist in something—that's all. He must study abroad, for everybody agrees that Italy knows nothing of the special branches. When he returns, the papa

will install him in a luxurious office. He will have a houseman in livery and an assistant in white linen: he will have
an X-ray machine and lots of expensive apparatus: everything he needs.

In the meantime the little doctor smiles and says nothing;
he smiles complacently at his mother's expansive goodwill;
he smiles with satisfaction at his father's fine plans. He
knows that he has nothing to worry about; he can choose
at his leisure the specialty that pleases him, and he can
choose it without troubling himself about it.

His specialty chosen, he will choose also the hospital or
institution, national or foreign, where he wants to perfect
himself. Then he will follow tranquilly a tranquil career,
assured of all scientific and professional advantages—a career
that will permit him to succor suffering humanity—without too much trouble.

Unhappy are the graduates who have no financial means
. . . and that was precisely my situation.

I returned to Milan with my family, carrying my
diplomas and plenty of felicitations, and rich in hopes but
without money. My examinations at an end, my income
suffered: for while a student, I enjoyed a money scholarship from the Congregazione di Carità which ceased as soon
as I had finished my university career. We nevertheless
took a five-room apartment in Milan, in the Via Santa
Sofia, on the banks of the Naviglio.

These five rooms were ill suited to a doctor; they were
all in a row, opening into each other. The first was divided in half by a partition which separated a little kitchen
from a corridor that served as an antechamber, and which
led to a small room used as a dining room; then came a

poky little hole that had to serve as my office, after which came two bedrooms: one for my brother and myself, the other for my mother.

How to receive clients was a difficult problem, for to reach my so-called office one had to go through the dining room. We found a practical solution by fixing my hours for consultation a good distance from mealtimes: thus the dining room could be made into a waiting room. It was arranged that during these hours the family should stay in their bedrooms.

We might have saved our energies, for no clients showed up. The dreams of paid work vanished so quickly that one day my mother and I exchanged glances, with despair in our eyes. Clearly, I had to come to some decision—and at once. I opened a medical journal, sought the POSITIONS OPEN column, and found that they wanted a parish doctor at Rozzano, on the Naviglio. I gathered my papers and diplomas together, and presented myself at the town hall.

But a cold reception awaited me: there were already eighty applicants, and I was the eighty-first. The secretary gave me the onceover, and let me understand that they would chose only someone who had already several years of practice behind him. I was far too young, I looked unimposing, quite unlike a doctor, in fact. Nevertheless, he asked whether I had powerful connections and good recommendations. I took my diploma from my pocket, and gave it to the secretary: it was my only recommendation. He, it seemed, was little impressed by the congratulations of the examiners, for he merely shrugged his shoulders, threw me a compassionate glance, and said nothing.

I realized that I was wasting my time, so I retrieved my papers, and returned home, there to seek refuge in my study. I felt discouraged, and my throat was parched with bitterness. Why had I hurried so to finish my course? What good was my scientific knowledge, anyhow?

When I think back to this first professional disillusionment, I can scarcely keep from laughing, and I truly believe that had I got that job as parish doctor at Rozzano, I probably would have rotted there in the midst of its flooded meadows and rice fields, bronzed by the sun and flushed by the wine.

Fortune had actually done me a good turn, but at the time I had not the sense to realize it.

My mother consoled me. Since the most wretched country parish repudiated me, we would have to make the best of it. Besides, Uncle Emilio would help me. He was mother's brother. A physician at Milan, in the suburb of San Gottardo, beyond the Porta Ticinese, he was the object of my admiration, and even of my envy. And he was indeed an enviable fellow: a practice in a Milan suburb; a sure stipend, with extra money coming in from well-to-do private clients. When he came home at noon, his pockets were full of clinking coins; every visit meant money, and he had plenty of patients in one day.

Of course, he worked unceasingly, and he was often roused from his warm bed at night. I soon saw that his life was not what it was reputed to be when I substituted for him during the Christmas holidays. The deputies were paid by the Milan township board at the rate of six liras a day, and they had to sleep at the dispensary.

And so, during my uncle's absence, I lived in his house, with an electric bell above my bed. I got a great satisfaction even from filling in for my uncle in this unimportant little suburb: I felt like a great authority, holding the lives of the villagers in the palm of my hand.

In the morning, I went in the drugstore, and got my daily visiting schedule, twenty or thirty calls, sometimes more.

"Good Lord," I ejaculated the first time, "how can Uncle make all these calls in one morning?"

Remembering that the famous Professor Forlanini, at the University, used to require as much as a week in studying a case, and sometimes more, I concluded that Uncle Emilio must be a very able clinician. At any rate, he must have thighs of iron! The hardest part of his job was not the call itself: it was the constant going up and coming down stairs, negotiating the four or five flights of the poor tenements, sometimes to end up in the cramped, airless attic into which the sun never penetrated, but from which the most indescribable odors emanated.

I figured that all these flights would, if added together every day, correspond to a stiff Alpine climb. Sometimes I joked with the druggist about these infernal climbs, and he assured me that my uncle, being a strong and wiry fellow, made every visit he was supposed to. But there was another physician in the same neighborhood who perplexed me sorely. He was as fat and round as a full moon, and weighed as much as an elephant. No stairs for him, I can assure you. He had someone outline the patient's symptoms to him, and sometimes, standing in the courtyard of a tenement, he would examine the tongue of a patient who was almost falling out of a window, four floors up. Then he would go on to his next strange visit, after leaving his prescription with the janitor.

All these Alpine visits worked up an appetite, and when I returned home at noon I was as hungry as a bear. But I

was due at the infirmary at one o'clock, and so had little
time to digest my lunch. And in the dingy little waiting
room in the town hall were assembled a crowd of from
forty to fifty people whom I had to attend, and to each I
had to give advice, attention, and, particularly, a prescription.

My poor art of medicine, what temples you hide yourself
in!

But my worst stint came at night. It was practically impossible to get a good night's rest in my uncle's dispensary.
Do not think that I was roused only for serious reasons:
they called me on the slightest pretext. I shall never forget
one Christmas night. I had eaten a hearty dinner in the
bosom of my happy family, and after the magnificent re-
past, with its heroic turkey and traditional sweetmeats, I
had returned to the dispensary. It was about midnight, and
bitterly cold. Snow was falling in great flakes, but the rule
was strict: I had to sleep at the dispensary. I lay down and
fell immediately into a heavy sleep. Suddenly the bell over
my cot rang. I jumped out of bed, and tottered to the window: a gust of wind chilled me to the bone . . . I lost
consciousness.

I have no idea how long I lay there, probably only a few
moments, for I was recalled to my senses by the continued
ringing. I lifted my numb body from the ground, wrapped
myself up, and went to the window to ask what was
wanted. Two people were outside chattering with cold,
even though they were well muffled up. They told me
that I had to hurry to a house on the outmost confines of
the parish. Was it serious? Certainly, the patient was in
agony. I pulled on my clothes as fast as I could. The house
belonged to a rich cheese merchant, one of whose guests

had taken ill after a heavy meal. They had put the sick man on a divan, and he had just thrown up a filthy mess of food and wine.

I approached the patient: an odor of wine, of vomit, and of gastric juice soured the air. I inspected him. It seemed that he was suffering merely from indigestion, but as his pulse was rather weak, I told the family I would return the next day. And I did return, but the patient had recovered, and had gone home.

The woman who opened the door thanked me drily, and handed me an envelope which I slipped into my pocket. I flew down the stairs, and tore open the envelope. It contained . . . try to guess, dear reader . . . one whole lira.

I had been awakened on Christmas night, I had risked pneumonia, and I had made two distant calls—in order to treat a drunkard! And all for one measly lira: in other words, less than the cost of a single bottle emptied in the course of a convivial evening.

I smiled bitterly, and involuntarily I recalled the savage verses of Fusinato: *Arte più misera, arte più rotta. . . .*

Being Uncle Emilio's deputy had somewhat chilled my ardor; the envy and admiration he inspired in me had also abated. Meanwhile, my predicament was just as bad as ever, and I scarcely knew which way to turn.

Of course, I was registered at the Central Hospital, but though that huge organization was the best school for seeing all sorts of illness and for getting a practical background, it did not put money into my purse. An assistant was paid one lira and nine centissimi a day, but to reach that exalted status one had to pass through the grades of interne and practitioner, without pay. Even then one could be appointed only after passing an examination that was held only every three or four years.

A hospital career seemed then like a luxury: a philanthropic affair for rich gentlemen. I felt mighty discouraged, but one day a fine idea came to me: I would confer with my former teacher, Professor Mangiagalli. It was a hard decision for me to reach, for I stood in awe of this really eminent man. But I gritted my teeth, and called on him. He received me kindly, and listened to my story. For a long time he pondered: he seemed to be thinking back to the difficulties of his own youth. At last he spoke, though rather more to himself than to me:

"The highest wisdom of man is knowing how to wait."

Then he said briskly, "I cannot help you very much, but at least I can recommend you at the Obstetrical Station of which I am the head. I do not think there is a post vacant at present, but take this note to Doctor Ferri, and he will do all he can for you."

With the precious note clutched tightly in my hand, I practically backed out of his presence, and ran all the way to Dr. Ferri. He, to tell the truth, did not seem overjoyed to see me. He read the note, shook his head, and said, "I'm sorry: there is no vacancy. However, hang up your hat. You are sure to learn something here, and you might come in handy during an emergency."

Thus I joined the staff of the Obstetrical Station.

The Obstetrical Station was then at the height of its fame and usefulness. Founded by Alessandro Cuzzi in the very heart of Milan as a relief station for pregnant women, it filled a definite need in the life of a great city that was growing in population by leaps and bounds.

A group of enthusiastic doctors had answered Cuzzi's call to arms, and they took turns living on the premises in the Via Unione, ready day and night to answer any call. The poor received free treatment. Dr. Attilio Ferri was the eldest of these volunteers, and he gave himself to the work body and soul. Obstetrics was more than a science and art to him: it was the beginning and end of his life.

A confirmed bachelor, he was crusty but kindly at heart; uncouth in appearance, he was amazingly genial. Whatever cynicism he affected was on the surface, and his honesty was proverbial. He stoutly boasted that he was an epicure, but he was always ready to deny his own comfort to do the slightest service for anyone. He wanted to be superior to his emotions and feelings, but actually the man was so brimming over with love for all, especially for children, that when he died they marked his grave with the figure of a little child: doubtless the symbol of all the children whose lives he had saved.

He despised pure science, but he had such a wide practical knowledge of cases, and particularly of obstetrical technique, that he had virtually revolutionized operating procedure, things of which no one else had ever thought. He was the master of details, and this talent was so native to him that he thought it native to all, though actually it constituted a veritable treasure on which his confreres drew inexhaustibly.

This man, so wise and good, received me unwillingly (he growled at Mangiagalli's cheek the whole time), and then presented me to my future associates. He took me with him on some of his calls, gave me some good advice, and generally undertook to guide me. Then I realized that the Obstetrical Station was a perennial source of valuable instruction. I saw the difference between surgery as practised in hospitals and clinics and as practised by the overworked, harassed general practitioner. I saw things that were almost miracles performed by the two small instrument cases: those for operations, those of hemorrhages. And I got a glimpse of strange corners of Milan whose very existence I had never suspected.

Chapter IV

VARIATIONS ON AN OBSTETRICAL THEME

OBSTETRICS IS WITHOUT DOUBT THE MOST MOVING AND, ALSO, the most fatiguing of all the medical specialties. It offers the greatest satisfaction, but it demands the hardest sacrifices.

The obstetrician called in during a childbirth comes in the rôle of a savior. He is a hero, a worker of miracles who will save two lives at one time: the mother and the child.

The first time I went with Dr. Ferri, I was transfigured with enthusiasm for my calling. The case was in a way unusual, but at the time I was so green in the business that I stood by absolutely petrified with admiration.

A midwife had called for help in the case of a young married woman, whom we found in her first childbed. The birth had proceeded smoothly until the so-called rupture of the amniotic sac, when there suddenly appeared, at the entrance of the vagina, a tiny hand: the baby was coming into the world shoulder first. The midwife was terrified, all the more because she should have felt the baby's unusual position in the womb sooner. Her fears were communicated to the relatives, and in a short time the whole household was in the grips of terror.

But the Obstetrical Station was ready. Dr. Ferri, followed by myself, who was to assist him, and the trembling

44

husband, who was slightly paler than a corpse, hastened to the house.

I pass over the welcome that awaited us. The scene of a difficult childbirth always has an aspect of tragedy that, to the seasoned obstetrician, is familiar to the point of banality. But it was all new to me: the atmosphere of terror, excitement, nervous tension; the outcries of the patient, the pleas of the relatives; all the noise and confusion. And it is in the midst of such an inferno that the obstetrician must perform his miracle. He must keep calm, not lose his head, inspire courage and faith, and, finally, dominate the situation.

Ferri was master, all right. One look, and he understood the case. First, he listened to the beating of the fetal heart: it was beating, yes . . . but growing feebler every second. . . . He had to act quickly. A rapid disinfectant, a lightning preparation. In a few moments the change in position was accomplished: the baby was now headed properly for his entrance into the world, and soon a feeble whimper indicated the good news to the family: *I am the life.*

The scene changes. Those who wrung their hands now cry with joy. The husband wants to kiss the obstetrician. They all crowd around to admire the small newcomer. The young mother lies there pale and exhausted; she cannot utter a word, but as soon as she gets her strength back, she thinks first of her baby. When they show it to her, she smiles happily at the miracle, and the look on her face is the kind, one suspects, they wear in paradise.

I witnessed this silently, but I was, none the less, absorbed and moved. I was not yet accustomed to such sights, and could think only of the doctor's lofty mission, and of the high art that guided him in the performance of such wonders.

On the way back, I couldn't keep up the pretense of professional restraint. I warmly congratulated Dr. Ferri. He burst out laughing, and said, "But that's nothing at all. That's not obstetrics! You haven't seen eclampsia. That's a real horror. And there's hemorrhage of the placenta, ruptured uterus. . . ."

My education in horror began with eclampsia.

If our talented novelist, Annie Vivanti, had studied obstetrical pathology before writing *I Divoratori*, she would have called the children of man not devourers, but poisoners. For before imbibing the maternal milk, the baby, waiting to be born, intoxicates the mother. He intoxicates her by pouring into her bloodstream a thousand poisons: the residue of his own metamorphoses.

If the maternal organism is strong and healthy in its defensive organs, it can transform and eliminate this residue, partially, at least, through the liver and kidneys. But if these organs are too weak and too delicate, then the poisons, neither destroyed nor eliminated, stay in the maternal blood, circulating throughout the organism, and ending by contaminating even the nerve centers, whence rise those terrible convulsions which constitute the most dramatic manifestation of what we call eclampsia.

Thousands of biological details, thousands of theories and hypotheses may be arguable, but one thing is certain: the baby is the enemy and poisoner of its own mother. This is so true that the obstetrician, if he hopes to save the mother's life, must rid her immediately of her dangerous guest. Old Borsieri wrote, *"Protinus danda opera est ut a foetu expeditissime liberentur,"* and the maxim still holds good today.

It nevertheless happens that, in a severe eclampsia, when the obstetrician has to resort to a so-called forced birth, he must perform an impressive and hideous-looking operation. First, he must open the still sealed mouth of the uterus, and, as soon as he has distended the neck sufficiently, seize the infant and draw him out, at any cost.

In this way they often save the mother, but more rarely the child. Sometimes, unhappily, neither survive. The gravity of the situation is such that the operation should be performed in a hospital or clinic, but sometimes the eclamptic attack comes so unexpectedly, and its circumstances are such, that the obstetrician is compelled to operate without delay.

Such was the first eclampsia I witnessed with my friend Ferri. I recall the circumstances perfectly.

The poor woman lodged in a modest apartment on the fourth floor of a tenement beyond the Porta Genova. She had been married a year, and the months of her pregnancy found her constantly happy and confident. During the last few days, however, she had difficulty in breathing; her vision seemed poor at times, and her head ached, but to these circumstances she paid little attention, thinking that they were normal concomitants of the last few days of pregnancy. Suddenly, one night, she was awakened by violent pains, the midwife was called, and the labor seemed to proceed normally until the very moment of delivery. Then, instead of being delivered, the woman rolled her eyes, her face hitherto so calm and serene assumed a hard, almost savage aspect, and her look became fixed. The convulsions began almost at once, and the face, neck, and arms quivered violently.

The poor midwife, who had witnessed these horrors, sent the husband to the Obstetrical Station. Meanwhile the patient lost consciousness, and she lay there, seemingly with all her senses deadened. Dr. Ferri and I had rushed out at the call, but while we were making the necessary preparations the poor creature had an even more violent attack than before, and this time she did not regain consciousness. Her strength was spent, and her face was tumid, flushed, congested.

Ferri performed prodigies of speed. He quickly dilated the uterus, applied the forceps, and drew out the infant, who had already begun to yell. But the young mother remained drowsy . . . there was a rattling in her throat. It was coma. . . . All our efforts, all our expedients, all the possible treatments suggested by science, applied in feverish haste, were vain. The poor woman died in a few moments.

Thirty years have passed, but I still recall that squalid bedroom, with that young woman, lifeless, the death pallor on her face, struck down in the supreme effort of her life. I still recall the cries of the husband, who fell on the lifeless form, and the shrieks of the woman's mother, which pierced the air like a sword, all mingling with the wailings of the infant wrapped in his swaddling clothes: the infant forgotten by all in the midst of this hubbub.

Such grief almost paralyzed me. It seemed suddenly to revive some scene through which I had already lived. Yes, I had witnessed such a scene, but where and when? I suddenly remembered a masterly and powerful work: *The Death of Rachel*, by Cignaroli, at the Venice Academy. The same scene, the same attitudes. . . .

I was rudely awakened from my meditations by a small but melodious voice coming from an adjoining room; it was the song of a canary, a friendly little bird who doubtless had solaced the dead woman during her pregnancy. He warbled and trilled. Was this his way of mourning, his instinctive lament for the dead?

Ferri and I silently replaced our instruments, and went just as silently. What else was there for us to do? Wearily we stepped into the carriage that had brought us only a few moments before.

Ferri was the first to speak. "Well, you've seen something. Keep right on being an obstetrician . . . if you have the courage."

And I really needed all the courage I could muster. When I think of my apprentice days at the Obstetrical Station, the ordeals I underwent, the difficult cases I worked on, I could write volumes.

I still recall my absurd terror of those violent and copious hemorrhages of premature placenta, when it seemed impossible that a woman could lose so much blood and, particularly, so much at one time. A competent obstetrician can, in such cases, save both mother and child, but only if he remains completely, brutally, calm.

Think, too, of the indescribable horror attending the embryotomy of the living fetus: a sad necessity which, theoretically, should not occur to the modern obstetrician. Practically, however, it is occasionally necessary in domiciliary cases.

But nothing surpasses in drama the Caesarean operation performed on a dead woman. This unhappy task never fell to my lot, but one of my confreres was not so lucky, and I still recall his agitated voice as he told his experiences.

He was just finishing his round of hospital visits when a woman of the most exceptional appearance was brought in. She was very short, her belly was tremendous, her flushed face suggested cyanosis, and she seemed to walk with difficulty. Her breathing, or rather, gasping, seemed to denote, along with her blue lips, a grave circulatory disease, possible heart trouble. A midwife, suspecting twins from the size of the woman's belly, had sent her to the hospital.

The poor creature had come, but on the way she had so much difficulty breathing that she scarcely reached the door. She was admitted at once. Suddenly her face drained of its color, and she lost her senses. Then she died.

Diagnosis was simple: an obvious case of cardiac syncope, but another painful problem intervened at once. Listening at the abdominal wall, my colleague found that the creatures in the uterus were living, and would live for some moments before sharing their mother's fate. The circumstances were by no means propitious for a Caesarean section. Assistants were lacking, and there was not even time for using the proper disinfectants. But the necessary instruments were there.

And so my colleague, making a quick decision, drew out his surgical knife, cut the abdominal wall, and opened the enormous uterine cavity. Two handsome infants were drawn from the womb: they were not only living, but lusty. They were sent immediately to the foundling hospital, and there they grew up, robust and healthy.

My friend confided to me that he had almost been overcome with terror before performing the operation. He had to work on a human being who was still almost throbbing with life, and then only under the most awkward circumstances and without preparation. If he waited, the life of the babies was endangered. Worst was the gnawing doubt: was the woman really dead? Suppose it was merely a case of apparent death—a fainting spell with the appearance of syncope? But he had to proceed, and the best he could do was to work as though he were operating on a living person.

But the woman gave no further sign of life.

When a friend of mine, a distinguished lawyer, found that I was writing this record of my surgical life, he encouraged me, and said, "A lot of novelists will read your book. It's just the kind of material they're looking for."

And I really often felt, during my years at the Obstetrical Station, that a writer could have gleaned richly by following me on my rounds, especially at night. Even now there passes before my eyes, like a cinema vision, all these varied environments, from the fine mansion to the most miserable attic room, from the modest worker's apartment to the squalid den of vicious and perverted outcasts.

Milan is a rich city, and since the last decade of the nineteenth century it has been an important center. But like any metropolis, it has its seamy side. Our calls often came from wretched neighborhoods, from evil-looking tenements where dire poverty was wedded only too often to the most unspeakable filth. Rooms where eight or ten people lived together; places so small and so crowded with furniture that there was not room to operate. Operate, did I say? . . . One could not lay aside his coat and vest without danger of infesting them with vermin.

In these cubbyholes he often had to resort to surgical methods of great delicacy and, even, of precariousness. Once, in order to perform a curettage, I had to stand inside a wardrobe, because there was no other room. Sometimes, as I was operating, and the woman was groaning with pain, I suddenly would see a head rise from a nearby cot: the sleepy head of a hitherto unseen child.

And what poverty, what wretchedness!

I shall never forget a certain icy January night, when my services were demanded for a premature twin birth in the Via Santa Lucia.

I jumped into a ramshackle and lurching cab, through which circulated an icy current of air that would have frozen an ox. The windows were sheeted with frost, and I thought that the poor devil of a husband who had come to fetch me would turn into an icicle.

We finally arrived—it was three o'clock at night—at a house buried in silence and gloom. The husband, with my surgical kit under his arm, opened the house door, and we began to ascend a staircase lit by one feeble light that was even more sinister than the enshrouding darkness. After many flights, our journey ended in a corridor. My companion opened a little door, and showed me into a garret whose only piece of furniture, worthy of the name, was a kind of marriage bed. Over the bed was a window so badly closed that the wind came whistling and howling through the room.

In that icy room, where I had to take off my coat, wash myself, disinfect myself and my instruments, and operate, I began by examining my patient. When I threw back the bedclothes, imagine my surprise when two or three sparrows flew out. When I fixed the pillow, a chaffinch flew away, and as I lifted up a pillow case I disturbed a black-bird.

I looked at my patient in amazement, and she explained. Her husband sold tame birds, and so the room had been turned into an aviary. But as the aviary had become an ice-box, they had hidden themselves under the bedclothes to get away from the cold.

And so I operated in the presence of these friendly little fellows. They were far more fortunate than I, for they were tucked in among the warm covers.

I should add that the twins I delivered that night were not only stillborn (for the mother was syphilitic), but they already were putrefied. At least they were lucky not being born into that desolate world of their diseased parents.

But this was not the only time animals witnessed my operations.

Some time after, late one cold Carnival night, I was called to a fair shed near the Porta Genova. That time-honored institution was then at its height: a collection of noisy, gayly painted huts, on the bastions of the old town; cages full of wild beasts, shooting galleries, puppet shows, freaks of nature, merry-go-rounds—a veritable hurly-burly of music, outcries, lights, and strong smells.

It was three o'clock at night, and I was just settling down to sleep when the bell above my bed made me jump up. A middle-aged man, dressed like a bum, and stammering an incomprehensible dialect of Italian, said that I was wanted at once. He also had a note from a midwife who explained that it was a case of violent hemorrhages following a three-month abortion.

I hurried into my clothes, and followed the fair man. He

had a hard time answering my questions, but slowly it developed that he was speaking of his wife—or at least of her who shared his bed: a snake charmer attached to the fair menagerie. During the show she had to work with a boa constrictor—a good sort (insisted my informant stoutly) that was well fed, and had never harmed a living soul. That evening, she had rolled it around her body, as usual, but the snake was not in its accustomed good humor. Instead of allowing the charmer's caresses, it began to crush her between its coils.

They had at last freed the poor woman, with the aid of the other tamers, but after this deathly embrace she had been seized with violent abdominal cramps, followed by a severe hemorrhage. They had carried her at once to her cot, and had called a midwife.

And so, at last, we reach the fairground. At this time of night all is plunged in darkness—it is like being in an encampment of nomads. The silence of the night is broken from time to time by strange elephant trumpetings, roars, squeals, howls, and piercing cries.

We are near the menagerie. My guide, with the surgical kit under his arm, threads his way among the sheds, until we reach the most crowded part of the encampment. I see a kind of house on four wheels, with temporary stairs giving access to an entrance platform on one end. A narrow shaft of light from the doorway discloses a group of people who are talking softly in a foreign tongue. Strange faces and costumes: there is a woman dressed like a lion tamer; a mustachioed man dressed like a ringmaster, though his face is painted like a clown's. As soon as they see me, they make way.

I mount the stairs, the fair wagon creaking and lurching

with every step. An acrid odor fills the air: the smells of animals, the sour stink of wild beasts, the odor of tetanus. I hesitate to enter this lair . . . I seem to be treading on serpents. A nameless fear overcomes me, in the midst of this stench, of this dirt, in this polluted atmosphere. But this is no time for indulging myself. I square my shoulders, and enter the tiny interior lit dimly by a single oil lamp.

The midwife receives me with a sigh of relief. Diagnosis is easy: it is simply a miscarriage in the third month of pregnancy . . . but the hemorrhage is excessive. To remove the poor creature to a hospital is unthinkable. I must operate at once, if I am to save her. But how? I have often worked in confined quarters, but never in such a hole as this. The woman lies on a kind of bunk such as they use in boats: I cannot even get her in the right position. And where can I wash and disinfect myself? I have a pair of washbasins put on the platform, and there, after taking off my coat, I wash myself in the icy water. Then by the dim lamplight I apply the speculum, and begin my work.

But while I am bending over the patient, I feel something moving between my legs . . . something that grasps my ankles. Can it be a snake? It certainly can—probably that fine fellow that brought on the miscarriage. I recoil in terror, but fortunately the hobo husband is there to save me. It turns out to be a small female monkey. At its mistress' cries of anguish, it had rushed from its hiding place to defend her, and had grabbed on to my leg. The hobo gives the monkey a box on the ears, and it runs away snarling and gnashing its teeth. Finally it jumps on to a little trapeze hanging from the ceiling, and there it sits attentively watching my proceedings.

At last I can continue my surgical task in peace. . . .

The woman is delivered of the embryo . . . and tamponed . . . and saved.

It is my turn to sigh with relief. I retire to the platform transformed into a dressing room and a disinfectory. Again I wash myself, along with the female tamer, the clown, the ringmaster, and a magician, who has wandered over from a nearby shack. I return to the interior, and assure myself that everything is all right, and that the woman is out of danger. Then I gather my instruments together. But they are not all there: I lack the two most important—the speculum and the curette.

The midwife knows nothing about it; she has been making the sick woman comfortable and clean. Nor has the husband touched them, for he has gone out to get a cordial for his wife. No one else has been in the room . . . the thing is incomprehensible.

Where, then, are my missing instruments? We look around us, and hunt for them under the bed, under the mattress, everywhere. All in vain, until . . . until we hear a slight tinkle from above. As we all gaze up at the perch, we break into uncontrollable fits of laughter, and even the patient, weak as she is, joins in.

The monkey is sitting on its trapeze, and brandishing the speculum in one hand, and the curette in the other, is trying to imitate the motions I had used in the operation.

But vice impressed me even more than misery. I was present at whole scenes from the *Grand Guignol*: actual pages out of the romance of crime.

One autumn night I was sleeping in my little room at the Obstetrical Station, when I was roused by a prolonged ringing of the night bell. The attendant—old Gregorio—rose, and a bit later came back to tell me that I was wanted.

As he was rolling his eyes in his most clownish way, I knew something was up.

"Anything special?" I asked, rubbing my eyes.

The old fellow chuckled, and whispered into my ear.

"The devil!" I exclaimed. What a business . . . !

"You'd better hurry. It seems to be a serious case: there's a note from the midwife."

He handed me a crumpled bit of paper on which was scribbled: "Please hurry—a very severe hemorrhage from a third-month miscarriage."

"Very well."

I dressed, and at the door an indescribable hag was awaiting me. Her profession was written all over her: she was the proprietor of the lowest type of whorehouse in the Via Vetraschi, the dregs of the Piazza Vetra, itself the center of one of Milan's most notorious districts.

We got into a cab, and the woman told me her story. That very evening, quite late, when the establishment was full of customers, a young girl was seized with a severe hemorrhage while she was entertaining a client. Amid all the excitement, they had sent at once for the nearest midwife, but her arts had been useless, and she had insisted on calling an obstetrician.

The woman thanked me for hurrying. I was a fine fellow. . . . "Doctor, if you could only see the flow of blood! Can you save her? The worst part of it is that the establishment is full. . . . Do everything you can, so long as you do it cautiously, silently." And to the devil with the cost—she would pay royally.

We arrived. The cab stopped in an alley, and we paused in front of a door studded with huge iron nails. We entered.

A vaguely musty smell filled the vestibule, and I hurried upstairs. But before arriving at the scene of the disaster, I got a glimpse of a kind of sitting room filled with half-naked women and with men both old and young, all barely distinguishable through the clouds of smoke. The odor of tobacco and human sweat mingled with the sinister medley of cries, roars, and bestial laughter.

I passed upstairs, arrived in a corridor, and was shown into a tiny room. A young and still lovely woman was lying on a bed. Her face would have been extremely pale if it had not been so heavily painted, and the red of her cheeks and lips contrasted strangely with her waxen and almost cadaverous body.

The woman was still half dressed, not in clothes, but in many-colored veils, such as a ballerina or a blues singer might wear. The bed was soaked with partly coagulated blood. Around the poor girl, a few of her friends were standing, trying to comfort her. All were just as painted, just as scantily clothed. It was a strange contrast of a bacchanal and death, and the heavy scent of cheap perfume heightened the obscene picture.

The midwife turned to me, and assured me that she had found the girl in a lake of blood. After making a diagnosis with difficulty, she had tried to stop the flow with a tampon, but unsuccessfully. She was at her wit's end.

Quickly and silently I laid aside my coat, and disinfected myself. The midwife was right: it was a miscarriage.

I operated quickly, then used the tampon.

Not a single person in the room so much as whispered a word, but through the walls I could hear a confusion of whispered words, murmurs, kisses, the rough voices of the men mingling with the laughter and groans of the women.

At times, at the height of this sexual symphony, my surgical instruments would interject a steely note of dissent.

But the woman did not speak, she did not groan; she did not even cry out when I scraped the uterus. She was too exhausted. She could only murmur a single phrase to one of her friends at the bedside: "The priest."

At last the operation was over, and I worked like a demon to get some life into the patient. This I did, thanks to injections and hypodermics. In two hours the pulse had become normal: the woman was saved. I gave the midwife my parting instructions, put back my instruments, and left the room. The stairs were dark . . . silence reigned over the establishment. Dawn showed in the east, and the customers had gone home. As I turned into the shadowy lane, I rubbed against a black form. Who could it be: a late customer or one of the many criminals of the Piazza Vetra quarter?

I wheeled about. There was nothing to fear: it was only the priest who had been summoned. He peered into my face, as though to ask a question.

"I think she's out of danger," I said. "Anyhow, Father, you've been called. Why not go in? . . . The place is horrible, I know, but the woman needs you. . . . Stairway to the right, first floor, on the corridor. . . . Good night."

By this time the reader is probably asking how I dared to go alone at night into the most dangerous sections, and even into the most evil byways of those sections. Some of my colleagues carried arms, so why didn't I? Well, I just trusted to luck, although I was once in a pretty bad spot.

One Carnival night I was at my accustomed post in the Obstetrical Station when I received the report of a miscar-

riage in a street near the Corso Genova. I knew the place—
it was a huge workers' tenement, with the doors of the
apartments opening onto long, cheerless corridors. The
thunderous silence of this vast building seemed deafening
as I climbed the steps to the fourth floor. The corridor
stretched out forbiddingly, all its doors closed. No, one was
half open . . . I could see a feeble gleam of light. From
the interior came murmurs, groans, pathetic lamentations.

The first room was empty, but I could see the lighted
room beyond another door. Thence came the confusion.

I entered, with my heavy instrument case in my hand,
and stared. . . . I saw an elderly man fighting with a very
fat woman. It was a very strange battle, fought amid furious shrieks and curses, with an obbligato of prayers and
lamentations performed by a very pale and frightened
young woman, who was lying stretched out on the bed.

I stood spellbound at this strange sight, not quite certain
what course to pursue. What hell had I come to? What had
happened to me? While I stood there with my eyes pop-
ping, the man saw me, and forgetting all about his victim,
rushed at me with murder in his eyes. I was paralyzed with
astonishment. Then I came to, dropped my case of instruments, and defended myself the best I could. At last I col-
lared the fellow, and pushed him out into the corridor,
closing the door from the inside.

Now I was shut up in the same room with two women.
I had come to do my duty, and I did not know what was
expected of me. But I soon did know. . . .

The young woman on the bed had miscarried after two
months; the older and stouter woman was the midwife who
was helping her. The madman was the patient's father

who had made the mistake (common with fathers) of thinking his daughter's virtue unassailable, and who had been disillusioned when, on returning from work, he had found his daughter in the throes of a miscarriage, with the midwife helping her.

It was a jolt. The poor fellow—one cannot help pitying him—had taken leave of his senses, and, not knowing whom to blame, had started on the midwife, who naturally was perfectly innocent. Just at that moment I stood on the threshold. The father seeing a young man—this was many years ago—enter without so much as a "Please, sir," had taken me for the guilty cause of the situation: the girl's fiancé or lover. Without waiting for an explanation (that was another mistake, too), he had charged me. I could see that nothing short of murder would satisfy him.

Fortunately he was not armed, otherwise I might not be here to tell the tale. After an exhausting struggle I pushed him into the corridor, and locked the door. When I knew the story, I still felt somewhat alarmed, and I thought rather sorrowfully of the risks the obstetrician runs. Then I tried the door again, and began to work.

Still bruised and numb, I disinfected my hands and my instruments, and delivered the poor young woman. But now another problem arose. How could I leave, how could I return to the Obstetrical Station? The madman was doubtless lurking in the corridor. . . . All my fears were perfectly reasonable, but yet I had to come to some decision: I could not wait until morning. I summoned up my courage, and cautiously opened the door into the corridor.

A long shadow stretched across the floor—even that was frightening. But I did not stop to convince myself that there

was no danger. A very proper, very timorous young fellow,
came up to me. "Is she all right?" he asked respectfully.

The swine! He was to blame for it all.

When I told my story at the Obstetrical Station, and
showed my bruises, my colleagues burst into loud guffaws,
and my good teacher, Dr. Ferri, scolded me for not carrying a revolver.

"One never knows," he said. "Heavens knows what
would have happened to two of our colleagues, some time
ago. They were called for a placental hemorrhage, and the
patient lived in one of those districts that make one shudder to think of them.

"The woman was in the ninth month of her first pregnancy. The child was coming out shoulder first, the dila-
tion of the uterus was incomplete; the hemorrhage, as in
all premature-placenta cases, was excessive. A very serious
problem, and made more so by the unhygienic conditions
surrounding the patient. She lived in the worst kind of
tenement beyond the Porta Tenaglia, many flights up, and
in the dirtiest sort of rooms.

"Of course, we tried our best: the woman was put to
sleep, and then we performed the usual Braxton-Hicks operation—performed it so brilliantly, in fact, that the operator, after correcting the fetal position and convincing himself that the baby still lived, began to think that he could
also save the mother. Actually, the little fellow emerged
safe and sound, but at the same time another, and more
copious, hemorrhage began. During delivery the uterine
neck had been punctured, and now the blood flowed in
buckets.

"The operator grew pale, and glanced significantly at

his confrere. He understood, and sent a messenger to the Obstetrical Station at once. Fortunately he did not open the note *en route*. For it contained the following not too enigmatic message: 'Come at once. Bring a not necessarily surgical instrument with you, and hold the cab at the door.'

"Meanwhile, things rapidly went from bad to worse. The blood continued to gush out despite all our efforts, and the woman got paler and paler. . . . At last the third assistant arrived: myself. Happily I had interpreted the note correctly, and had brought a good revolver. I arrived just in time to see the woman die, and to reassure my colleagues. The critical moment had arrived. The air was thick with cries, wailing, curses, and the inmates of the malodorous hive appeared at the window giving onto the outer gallery or crowded the corridor. Soon we heard the sinister cry: 'They have killed her!'

"Imagine our predicament. Persuasion was impossible— they would not listen to our words. We collected our instruments, and made for the stairs. There we had to run the gauntlet of the evil denizens of the place. What criminal masks, what curses, what blasphemies! I had my hand on the revolver, and that lent me courage and a certain self-possession. At last we reached the street, and bounded into the cab.

" 'Get going!'

"When we reached the Station we could breathe easily at last."

But my worst experience occurred in prison: in the vast old penitentiary of San Vittore. This time the midwife did not summon me as was usually the case, but my colleague and friend, Terzaghi, now the sole survivor of the glorious days of the old Obstetrical Station. He had been called, one cold January night, to treat an inmate, and had found a very serious case: an eclampsia in the seventh month of pregnancy.

The patient was a murderess—an admitted prostitute, but still young and beautiful. She was the mistress of an ex-convict, who had seduced her and made her pregnant, months previously. But one day the poor wretch found that her lover was two-timing her with another woman. She had sworn to be revenged, and one evening she surprised the guilty pair drinking together in a private room in a notorious tavern in the Via Arena. Mad with grief and drunk with thoughts of vengeance, she had rushed at her rival like a bomb, and had wounded her in the back with a knife. Then she had fainted, and when she woke up, she was in a cell in the San Vittore prison.

She had waited several months to be tried, and meanwhile her pregnancy advanced. Emotion, remorse, and grief, combined with the cold and moisture of the cell, had ruined her health. She developed nephritis, which culminated, one night, in a violent eclampsia.

They had called the prison midwife, and she had called for an obstetrician at once. My good friend Terzaghi could not handle the situation alone. He had exhausted all the resources of medical science, and yet, within a few moments, the patient had had three attacks of convulsions. He would have to resort to a forced birth, but he needed an assistant, at least to administer the anesthetic. He sent to the Obstetrical Station for help, and from there the cab had been sent on to my house.

A prison is a sufficiently melancholy spot at any time, but in the silence of the night it is shuddersome and frightening. The vast penitentiary was buried in abysmal silence; only the raucous voice of the sentinel was heard from time to time.

Inside, I entered a gloomy corridor . . . then came shadowy steps . . . then another corridor flanked with cells. Silence . . . the silence of a tomb, except that our steps awakened a sinister echo that reverberated throughout the vast and fearsome arena.

Finally we arrived at the cell.

The patient was lying on her back. The face was congested, contorted, the eyes were glazed. She had just had a convulsion: coma had intervened.

We had to act promptly.

It was impossible to operate there, so we carried the woman to the infirmary, and placed her in approximately the classical position. A real hospital bed was lacking, but we did our best. She was carried by two deputy nurses, both inmates of the prison: one a midwife who was serving time for performing an abortion, the other for thievery and receiving stolen goods.

The obstetrician, with his kindly, honest face, looked like Jesus between the two thieves. . . . I began to administer the anesthetic, while my colleague introduced the forceps after dilating the uterus. Deftly he extracted a seventh-month male infant who emitted a sad and despairing cry, as though protesting against the place into which he had been born.

But the cry was feeble, expiring. . . .

The kindly Terzaghi had foreseen all: the consummate obstetrician became the priest, and in a basin of pure water he baptized the little creature in the name of the Father, the Son, and the Holy Ghost. The infant sobbed feebly, then breathed a tiny sigh of relief before leaving the world of which he had seen so little, and that little so cheerless and sad. No doubt the mother would have followed him had not our energies saved her at the very last moment.

The infant was privileged. The mother had to remain behind to expiate her crime, exposed to opprobrium, grief, despair. . . . We resigned the patient to the midwife's and deputy nurses' care: our task was finished.

We collected our instruments, and went from this place of pain and suffering; again we traversed the cell-lined corridors . . . those dark and melancholy lanes. The cab stood at the door. We entered silently, and as silently drove to the Station.

A single thought weighed upon our minds like a relentless incubus: the horrible scene that we had witnessed.

Alma Venus! Coeli subter labentia signa
Quae mare navigerum, quae terras frugiferentis
Concelebras, per te, quoniam, genus omne animantum
Concipitur, visitque, exortum, lumina solis!

—Lucretius

To cause an abortion is murder.

The obstetrician truly commits murder when he extinguishes the life of the embryo in the womb, for the little being is more than a potentiality, he is a reality—a being who lives, and has a right to live.

The doctor should never kill; he should always give life and health: health to the mother, life to the product of the conception. Yet, in certain circumstances it is essential to kill the embryo. When? That is not easy to decide. In fact, it is so difficult that we are still disagreed about the propriety of interrupting the course of the pregnancy, and some even say that it is never proper.

This argument was under discussion at a recent congress of obstetricians convened in Milan in the lecture hall of the Istituto Mangiagalli. The discussion was extremely interesting—in fact, I cannot remember ever being more absorbed, or diverted, than at this congress. The most famous Italian obstetricians attended, as well as many medical and surgical bigwigs. The most eminent clinicians of the time spoke, but the interest of the discussion was heightened by the fact that, for the first time in an obstetrical congress, a representative of the clergy had been officially invited: Father Gemelli, the eminent rector of the Università Cattolica.

Feeling ran high—at times there was a real battle. The religious authority was irrevocably opposed to therapeutic abortion, no matter what the circumstances. And the obstetricians did not agree. Some supported Father Gemelli's views; others hesitated: in so violent an argument, they refused to take sides. But plenty remained lined up on the traditional side, holding that gestation, under certain conditions, may rightly be interrupted, at least in the present state of obstetrical science.

According to the traditional group, certain signs are clear, apparent, and well-defined: that is, certain illnesses, certain diseases, do not favor the woman giving birth. In such cases, if the obstetrician persists in allowing the gestation to proceed, he puts both mother and child in mortal danger. Under certain conditions (say the traditionalists), it can be fatal to hesitate. Their job is to save, and they save what they can . . . in this case, the mother.

On the other hand, other signs are less clearly interpretable. Pregnancy itself can cause grave disturbances, some of which have the appearance of actual diseases. And it is certain that if the obstetrician performs an abortion in such cases, these troubles will vanish.

Further, it is certainly true that by giving the woman patient and persistent care, it is possible to complete even a difficult pregnancy, and end by saving the baby, too. In doubtful cases (and there are many of them), the decision must be left to the judgment of the individual obstetrician, who depends on his trend of thought, his experiences, and the special circumstances.

If he is scrupulous, he may confer with his colleagues, and share the responsibilities with them. If he is less scrupulous, he takes matters in his own hands, and easily settles the question. And so he may find indications justifying abortion that colleagues might find inadmissible.

I recall that at the beginning of the World War, when the Germans had brutally invaded Belgium, the news went around that woman and girls had been violated and rendered pregnant against their will. At that time Professor Bossi, director of the university clinic at Genoa, lent his great authority to the dogma that in such cases, if the woman asks for an abortion, the obstetrician has the right to perform it.

This situation was very cleverly exploited by the novelists. Who does not remember, for example, Annie Vivanti's vivid *Vae victis?* This is the story of two women, the one married, the other engaged; both were violated by officers of the German army. They were rescued by the Red Cross, and sought refuge in England, where they first became aware of their condition.

The married woman burned with shame, first because

her own ideal of herself had been soiled. As a faithful wife and model mother, she felt outraged at having to break, even involuntarily, her marriage vows, and finally, as a Belgian woman, the thought of bearing German seed filled her with horror. She rebelled against such an enormity, and loudly asked to be freed. The priest listened to her prayer with horror, but the obstetrician, after a long struggle with his conscience, performed an abortion.

In the young woman, however, the voice of nature was strong. The father mattered little: the creature within her was hers. It lived, it had the right to live, and she lacked the courage to kill it. She sacrificed herself, her future, her love, her family—but she saved the baby.

Let us hope that such situations may not recur in the future, and that the heart and courage of the obstetrician may not be troubled by them. But it is no wonder that, by trusting too implicitly in *relative* signs, one arrives insensibly at criminal abortion. We call it criminal because morality condemns it almost everywhere, and so does the law in almost all civilized countries. There are, of course, certain countries where abortion is condemned by the legal code, but is winked at in practice.

I do not pretend that complaisant practitioners do not exist in all countries, and I will even admit that when a clever obstetrician wishes to perform an abortion, he can do so, and defy the law. In such a delicate and complex matter, what prevents him from pretending therapeutic reasons? And what prevents him from making the wrong diagnosis?

But the upright doctor, the scrupulous obstetrician, interrogates his own conscience, and does not compromise.

He heeds no argument: prayers, scandals, promises of rich rewards; he risks unpopularity without flinching.

I recall a disgusting incident that happened at the beginning of my career, and which impressed me so strongly I still remember it vividly, doubtless because it happened when I was young and inexperienced.

I was still living in that very modest apartment in the Via Santa Sofia, where my office was very small, and the patients few and very poor. I was sitting reading the paper in the so-called reception room, when the nurse informed me that a fine carriage had stopped before the door, and that its equally fine master was waiting to be received.

She showed him in. "You should see his clothes!" she whispered. I received him in my tiny office, and asked him to be seated. He was truly a grand signior, richly dressed, suave in manner, and still young. He sat down in the only easy chair, and sized me up: clearly he was embarrassed, and did not know how to begin. On my part, I was so surprised to be consulted by such a client that I thought the whole thing a dream. At last I asked how I could serve him.

He began to stammer. "A midwife gave me your address. She told me that you were extremely clever, and that you were just the man to handle an affair for me—an affair that is most delicate and confidential."

I listened in astonished silence: I did not suspect what was coming.

It was a matter that might have very serious consequences. A few months before he had chanced to meet a woman of the highest social position. They had met at the college where both of them were educating their

children. He was married—in fact, he had gone to see his
two sons at the seminary in a certain remote provincial
town. He had met the woman in the same waiting room,
and they had spoken of their children: for she too had a
son in the same academy. She was a widow, though still
young and beautiful. They chanced to miss the train back.
They stayed in the same hotel . . . there was only one.
It rained and rained . . . there was no other traveler at
the cursed inn. So, the thing had happened.

How? Well, he could remember nothing more, but
nothing could be more certain: it had happened. The next
morning they had returned to Milan, and had not seen
each other again. One fine day, however, he had received
a desperate letter, sent so imprudently that it almost fell
into his wife's hands. The poor woman announced that
she was pregnant. It was impossible to describe her agony
of mind: the thought of the possible scandal was a nightmare to her, and she feared its effects on her old parents,
especially on her extremely pious mother. She was afraid
to look her children in the face, so ashamed was she. She
would rather die than face the world after such a scandal.
In short, she wanted his advice . . . she thought herself
going mad, and capable of any crime.

The news had come like a thunderbolt, and he feared
that, sooner or later, his wife would find out. It would
mean ruin, scandal, dishonor for both families. . . . But
yet he was a gentleman, a man of honor. The evil had
been done, and they would have to bear its consequences.
He had tried to calm the lady, and had gone to consult a
midwife, who had given him my address.

After his confession the poor man slumped back in the
chair, and buried his head in his hands. I said nothing.

What did he want of me? Why this long preamble when he could have said everything in a few words. It was obvious that he wanted an abortion performed. And I was "just the man" for such a charming job. Who the devil was the midwife who had done me such an honor? Probably she knew my financial position, and thought I would yield easily. Well, she was wrong. I certainly had not worked and suffered to do such jobs. I would rather keep on being poor.

I rose brusquely, and he understood at once that he could hope for nothing from me. He rose, too, and went out.

I saw the man some months later in a public place, but we did not speak. As I had heard of no scandal about the two distinguished families involved, I suppose their honor had been safeguarded by a clever operator with less scruples than I had.

Six years had elapsed since my degree. My début had been anything but reassuring, but hard work had made me better off financially, and I could now look to the future with a certain tranquillity. When I think of those first six years I am amazed that my physical forces had been able to bear up under the strain.

I often passed the night at the Obstetrical Station, and I had begun my hospital career. After the examinations, I had become first assistant, then surgeon's aide. But this did not satisfy me: I nourished a love for pure science, sought to publish my works. At the end of 1906 I successfully passed the examination for surgeon's aide. It was then that I had to solve the dilemma: surgery or obstetrics?

I did not hesitate.

I loved general surgery: the great art which comprehends all the specialties, and from which all the specialties stem.

So, after mature reflection, one fine day I sent in my resignation from the Obstetrical Station. My colleagues were expecting it, but they were sorry to lose their "Maiocchino," as they called me. They said that they had given me birth, and also nourished me. So, in order not to lose me completely, they first named me honorary obstetrician, then consulting surgeon to the Obstetrical Station.

In the years that followed they gave me so many proofs of confidence and esteem that I cannot think of them without emotion and gratitude. They encouraged and bucked me up; they guided my first steps, and eased the way. Nothing is too good for them.

Chapter V

SURGERY, SCIENCE AND ART DIVINE!

WHEN I BEGAN MY SURGICAL CAREER AT THE CENTRAL Hospital at Milan, the operative art was fully developed. This very honorable profession, only recently restored to its proper status, had taken a long time to recover from the low estate and discredit to which it had been condemned by the bigots of the dark ages.

Ecclesia abhorret a sanguine, according to the decision of the Council of Tours in 1163, and that presumptuous ostracism had served to put surgery in a bad light, and many thought it accursed. As reputable doctors therefore long refused to perform any operations attended by loss of blood, surgery was abandoned to the empiricists: to the so-called barber-surgeons. The doctor rightly claimed everything that was fine and elevated in medical knowledge. His were the science and study of diagnosis and treatment, his the responsibility of interpreting the symptoms and making all decisions. However, when an operation was needed, he called in the surgeon: handling the bistoury and the lancet would have degraded him.

So surgery had become an abject art, while medicine was considered a liberal art, and the profession of the doctor a noble one. And the adepts of surgery reached their moral elevation at great cost. How many battles they had to fight with the doctors, who were under the powerful protection

74

of Saint Cosmas, as late as the time of Ambroise Paré, who could not be acknowledged *because he did not know Latin.*

To get an idea of these most curious controversies, it is enough to run through the publications of that age (the golden period of the Renaissance), as summarized in Diderot's treatise: *Lettre d'un citoyen qui n'est ni chirurgien nin médecin,* a milestone in the rehabilitation of surgery, since it ends with this prayer: ". . . *qu'il n'ait plus de chirurgiens, mais que les médecins et les chirurgiens réunis forment un corps de guérisseurs.*" He wished explicitly for surgery to be raised in the public esteem and for its offices to be entrusted no more to the blind exercise of manual operations. He wished surgeons to study disease, recognize symptoms, and undertake diagnoses.

Nevertheless, at the middle of the last century, the field of surgery was still most limited. Though no longer the *ancilla humillima medicinae,* this art was still insignificant. The surgeon busied himself almost exclusively with diseases of the joints, of the muscles, of the most accessible organs. The doctor, on the other hand, treated the internal organs, the intestines, and those very delicate parts which are more than ever reserved for clinical research.

Medicine was divided into internal medicine, which belonged to the physicians, and external medicine, reserved for the surgeons. The operative art acquired status and a solid basis with the rise of antisepsis and anesthesia, and as these powerful auxiliaries of surgery appeared together, its progress amazed even its most enthusiastic practitioners. It strode forward on seven-league boots.

Why this success? It is very simple.

Everyone knows that in the so-called bloody operations,

the surgeon makes artificial wounds which heal easily and cicatrize quickly, if they are not polluted by infectious agents. On the other hand, they do not heal, and they suppurate, when the tissues that constitute the lips of the wounds come in contact with infected substances. In other words, every wound, however important, is not dangerous itself, but becomes so when in contact with elements capable of effecting changes in the tissues. These elements are the microbes—infinitely tiny creatures—whose germs, usually contained in the air, are deposited on objects, on our hands, on everything about us.

Thus surgical wounds, harmless themselves, become dangerous in the presence of microbes. It was obvious to the pioneers of antisepsis that if they wished to avoid the dangers of infection, they must war against these noxious elements. Lister, founder of this novel surgical concept, introduced the use of certain substances which could kill microbes. These substances, in solution, are used to wash instruments, dressings, the operators' hands, and the tissues of the wounds.

I found operative technique at this stage, when I began my career. They used rivers of corrosive sublimate to wash the operating rooms, solutions of carbolic acid in the instrument basins (with what effect on the assistants' hands!), and foul-smelling iodoform powders on the wounds and sores. In some surgical centers they even saturated the air of the operating rooms with carbolic-acid vapor.

The results of the operations were more consistently successful, but one fact was inescapable: the antiseptics killed the germs, but also injured the essential parts of the tissues. Furthermore, they began to notice that though the use of antiseptics was effective in killing microbes wherever they were (in sores, for example, wounds already infected), they were useless in treating uninfected, or aseptic, wounds. In treating such wounds the surgeon must not touch with his bare hands either the instruments or the dressings of the infected areas.

It was then that they moderated the use of antiseptics, of the so-called microbicidal substances, and adopted asepsis. They contrived that in surgical operations all that comes in contact with the operator must be asepticized, or rid of infectious germs. This is easy enough for the instruments and dressings, much less so for the operators' hands. It was enough to put the former in boiling water, but the skin of the hands was notoriously hospitable to microörganisms, and it was difficult to get rid of them.

When I first began my surgical work, these poor hands had to be washed and disinfected in all ways, every half hour in warm water and soap, then in solutions of permanganate, oxalic acid, carbolic acid, and alcohol. . . . But the hands were always so full of bacteria that being plunged, after such treatments, in culture soups, they gave lodging to colonies of bacteria.

The problem of disinfecting the hands was not solved until a few years after I had taken my degree. It now seems as obvious as Columbus' egg, but I do not think I am exaggerating when I say that the use of rubber gloves marked one of the most notable conquests of operative technique. Gloves boiled or disinfected in the sterilizer protect the wound against the skin of the hands.

So asepsis was perfected gradually, and results were phenomenal. The operations hitherto considered most dangerous became safe; the most gaping wounds closed and healed quickly; obstetrical maneuvers formerly fraught with the greatest dangers now succeeded admirably.

Surgery leapt forward under my eyes; at the same time it found another resource that contributed to its rapid progress. I mean anesthesia, or the stopping of pain. Rather, I should say the perfecting of anesthesia, for efforts to soothe pain have had a long history. Giambattista della Porta said that toward the end of the year 1600 they made patients breathe a mixture of opium, henbane, mandrake, hemlock, and other drugs. However, the slumber was always problematical; furthermore, the Church condemned the narcosis as sorcery, and it was abandoned.

One shudders to think of the practice of surgery before the coming of anesthesia. Imagine the course of the most elementary operation—amputation of a leg, for example—on a conscious patient. Imagine the piercing cries of the patient writhing under the bistoury, and the agonizing pain caused by the oil and the boiling tar poured on the stump to prevent hemorrhage.

Silvio Pellico has related something similar in *Mie Prigioni*—the amputation suffered by poor Maroncelli is reminiscent of the cases described by my old teacher, Professor Bottini. He told me of lessons from the last years of his youth, when he had gone to Paris to study surgery. He had returned home completely disgusted. He had seen the patient, thoroughly conscious, twisting under the surgeon's hands, shrieking at the top of his lungs, and held down only with the utmost difficulty by the strong arms of the hospital aides. It was a real battle between the patient and the operators, and the spectacle resembled a scene in a torture chamber rather than a surgical operation.

Bottini felt such a distaste for these methods that he decided to give up, and indeed he retired to the Sappey Institute, in order to study anatomy. According to his own words, at least the cadavers no longer suffered.

Happily for the eminent surgeon and for the entire human race, the facts of anesthesia, first used in America in 1846, were published at this time. Like many great discoveries, anesthesia was the result of an accident. A dentist, William Thomas Greene Morton, happening to put a dressing, saturated with ether, into a patient's mouth, noticed that he no longer complained, and that he was sleeping peacefully. He repeated the test on another patient, and discovered that by making him inhale this substance, a deep sleep was induced during which he could perform any operation without the patient being at all conscious of it.

The discovery was sensational, and the good news was carried on the four winds. Today, in the General Massachusetts Hospital, at Boston, they still show the chair in which the first patient slept. In a short time it was found that other substances besides ether had the same property. When I began my career chloroform led the field. Since then there has been a veritable phantasmagoria of anesthetics and of means of anesthesia.

Besides narcosis, that is, general anesthesia, local anesthesia was developing and flourishing. Not satisfied with being able to put their patients to sleep, surgeons sought to operate painlessly on a conscious subject. They tried to substitute conscious for unconscious anesthesia. It was possible to render a certain part insensible by various agencies: freezing, local anemia, but especially by the use of certain substances that paralyzed the sensitive nerves. Among these the best known are cocaine, stovain, novocaine. . . . According to the regions of the human organism where these substances are used to paralyze the nerves, we speak of a spinal anesthesia, a regional anesthesia, a trunculary anesthesia, and so on.

During the years since taking my degree, I have seen all these various methods succeed one another, and I believe that I have myself tested most of them. It would be unwise to say that one is preferable to another. The truth is that the intelligent surgeon must know how to find the means that is best fitted to the case in point. Furthermore, since there are no two individuals absolutely alike, the operator must examine his patient with care, and, in view of the operation to be performed, choose the best means.

But no matter what choice the operator makes, the operation is painless: the patient is quiet, motionless, receptive, and the operation almost assumes the character of an anatomical lesson performed on a cadaver. It can be done calmly, without thought of time, and with relative ease.

The revolution in anesthesia that I witnessed constitutes a glorious epoch in the history of surgery. By means of asepsis and anesthesia regions and organs, formerly considered untouchable, have been attacked by operative technique: brain, kidneys, stomach, spinal marrow, bile ducts, and heart itself are now in the field of surgical exploitation.

The barriers between external and internal pathology have dwindled irremissibly, and the surgeon, master of the entire human body, can finally glorify surgery: "Science and art divine."

Chapter VI

MY HOSPITAL

It is hard to say just what a hospital means to a surgeon.

It is to him what a ship is to a sailor, a house to a woman, a theater to an actor, a church to a priest. If you can conceive of a sailor without a ship, or of a woman without a house, then you can imagine a surgeon without a hospital. For to him the hospital is, at once, the field of his activity, the school, the daily exercise ground. In the hospital the surgeon forms and perfects himself; in the hospital he experiments with new methods, and in the hospital he collects material for new studies, observations, publications. But if the surgeon chances to be a Milanese, and you speak of hospitals to him, you will see his face take on an expression of mingled satisfaction, tenderness, and pride.

There is but one hospital for the Milanese: *"Ca' Granda,"* the great dwelling, the house par excellence, always affectionately nicknamed, the vast hospice that treats all ills, and receives all ailing.

It is said that Francesco Sforza and Bianca Maria founded the Central Hospital, and these ancient Milanese rulers really donated a villa, on the Naviglio, and behind the apse of San Nazzaro: this villa and its outbuildings constituted the nucleus of the hospital. But the real creator of the Central Hospital were the Milanese themselves, who a century before had begun the building of the great cathedral—yes, the Milanese built the church, not Duke Gian Galeazzo, who merely lent his benevolent approval to the work. And just as the huge and marvelous cathedral represented the synthesis of an infinity of sacrifices, generosity, and renunciations, so the Central Hospital is a testimony and monument to the great Ambrosian heart.

If you do not believe it, go to the vast picture gallery, and look at the portraits of its benefactors: a steady line of philanthropists from 1476 to the present day. Generosity never ceased, not even in the leanest times.

When the question arose of building a house for the sick, the Milanese wanted to make it large and beautiful. Yes, beautiful even, for, if God and Mary had their superb temple, and if the Sforza tyrant had built for himself one of the finest castles in the world, it was no more than right that the sick should have a large and commodious house, very splendidly adorned.

They called in one of their most famous architects: l'Averulino, called Filarete, the same man who built the Sforza castle, and they gave him a free hand. He, on his part, gave them a masterpiece. Filarete built that palace which is still the marvel and delight of all, with its purest Renaissance arcades, its windows whose grace is the envy of artists, and its exquisite cornices. In 1600 they added another building, the gift of a single donor, Dr. Carcano. This was even more beautiful than the first; its architectural motives were inherited from Filarete, but it also boasted a large courtyard that would have adorned a royal palace. Then another philanthropist, Dr. Macchio, gave a third building, to complete this magnificent establishment.

Little by little the Central Hospital gained in beauty and

importance. Destined to receive the sick from the entire duchy of Milan, it naturally and rapidly assumed an exceptional importance. When I entered, in 1900, the activity was tremendous, but it was still confined almost exclusively to the glorious old building. Nevertheless, the requirements increased daily, owing to the rapid increase of population, both in the city and in the province. They had to add new buildings to the old fabric. The first of these bears the name of Alphonso Litta, because it was donated by his noble family.

This detached building, erected in the midst of the kitchen gardens adjoining the Via della Commenda, stimulated Milanese generosity, and soon other buildings were built and endowed, so that the wide kitchen gardens, between the bastions of the Porta Roma and the old hospital, no longer existed. There rose a long line of hospital pavilions, each finer than the others.

Further expansion was no longer possible. The administrative council of the hospital, led by the illustrious Della Porta, its president, planned to erect another hospital city beyond the town itself, near the suburb of Niguarda. After the work was completed, the vast old palace would be evacuated by the sick, and it would be restored to its pristine state of beauty, and kept as a relic, devoted exclusively to offices, picture galleries, libraries, and administrative departments.

I do not know what the future holds for *my hospital*. Its past was truly glorious, for since the Middle Ages all branches of medicine, not excepting surgery, have gained honor there.

Remember that even as late as the time of Lodovico il

Moro, the shadows of the Middle Ages had not yet lifted: superstitions of all sorts spawned and multiplied; sorcerers were accused of causing illness, and if they were caught, they were burned at once—a punishment viewed, until comparatively recent times, with complacency. Even the sainted Federico Borromeo approved of it.

The renowned Leonardo da Vinci, then at Milan, studied anatomy as well as other sciences, but when he wanted to dissect a specimen, he had to collect his cadavers secretly. The art or profession of surgery, as I have said already, was repudiated by the medical gentry, who did not care to soil their hands with blood. They gave up surgery to the quacks and empiricists, then called barber-surgeons. Surgery must have been in a sad state at the time. Ambroise Paré had not yet been born, and therefore practitioners knew nothing of the ligature of the arteries; they had to resort to oil or boiling tar to stop hemorrhages. We can get some idea of the primitive surgical methods used by reading the contemporary records.

Perusing the chronology of Luogo Pio, I found ordinances anterior to 1550, which speak of localities turned over to surgeons for their lectures. Another ordinance, of 1598, mentions surgical clinics attended by young men come there to study, and for whom special courses were organized. It would seem that a real school of surgery, however elementary, existed as early as 1687, in which year a decree of the council named a doctor to make autopsies, as well as to give a course in anatomy, either in Latin or in the common tongue, for young students. According to Decio, the beginnings of this school reach back to 1634.

It was the most disastrous chapter in Milan's history.

The people, groaning under the Spanish tyranny, suffered also from plague. In 1634 the town began to lift its head, but doctors, especially good doctors, were lacking. Then it was that a kindly man, Dr. Cristoforo Inzago, offered to practice surgery at our hospital, and to teach gratuitously barbers and under-barbers: *"Cirurgiam tonsoribus, et subtonsoribus, et aliis personis ipsius Hospitalis legendi, absque ullo salario."*

I must omit other details of this fascinating début. Suffice it to say that the chair of surgery (if it deserves the term), inaugurated through Inzago's generosity, was finally occupied by Calvi and by Biumi. The latter wrote a *Scrutinio teorico-pratico di Cirogia antica e moderna*, as well as a verse translation of Hippocrates' aphorisms *"pro ingenius medicinae tironibus."* I refer the reader to these documents if he wishes to get an idea of the surgery then practiced at the Central Hospital. Primitive and makeshift, not to say medieval, it certainly was, and so it remained until the coming of Bernardino Moscati.

His arrival on the scene marks a veritable signpost in the history of surgical art, and it is greatly to the credit of Venerando Capitolo, who wished to get rid of Barbieri, Norcini, Preciani, and all the quacks who then infested the place, that he invited Moscati to the hospital. He wanted surgery to be in the hands of a worthy doctor—a *collegiato* (as they said in those days), profoundly learned in all branches of medicine. So Moscati went to Milan from Pisa where he was chief surgeon and *incisore anatomico* at the university. At the hospital he used the Crociera del Prato (now the Sala Pio II). He at once bent his efforts to completing and renewing the surgical stores; then he reorganized the staff, and raised the scientific status of the hospital.

Not satisfied with his work, the new chief wished to go abroad to study the most recent developments in surgery, and this voyage bore fruit at once. He unified surgery, which was then divided into a thousand specialties (herniotomy, phlebotomy, lithotomy, etc.); he reformed operative technique; a real course in surgery was initiated to which Moscati, on his own accord, added a school of obstetrics. It is largely due to him and to our hospital that we can say today that Milan taught obstetrics and had an obstetrical clinic earlier than Pavia, and almost as early as Florence and Bologna.

The great surgeon died at the age of ninety-six, honored and mourned. He was the greatest figure in the history of our hospital, and it is truly strange that our Istituto has not voted a monument to the unifier of surgery, to the tireless champion of the hospital school. No statue commemorates him. And even the pavilion of gynecological surgery, which I have the honor to direct, is dedicated to Pietro Moscati, the son, and not to the father, Bernardino, admittedly the worthier and more renowned of the two.

But the father erected the monument in his own lifetime: his school. Pietro continued Bernardino's traditions, and he had worthy successors in Monteggia and Palletta.

Pietro Moscati was a man of quick understanding and deep learning, and yet he was not able to proceed with his scientific labors: politics disturbed his life, and paralyzed his activity. Monteggia added enormously to surgical lore, and his works are still quoted abroad—especially in France —though Italy herself has forgotten them. His *Istituzioni chirurgiche* was considered the best surgical treatise of the age. Palletta was responsible for the celebrated *Exercitiones Pathologicae*, so warmly praised by Scarpa.

So surgery flourished at the Central Hospital from 1700, and continued until 1849, the year of a strange, almost inexplicable event: the sudden creation of a faculty of medicine. This year the Austrians returned, and once again Lombardy groaned under foreign tyranny. Milan was declared in a state of siege. Among other humiliations, she had to submit to the closing of her universities. At once the Central Hospital, cheered on by the Milanese, organized a university school. The director and his chief lieutenants gave regular lectures in all branches of medicine without pay. This fine school remained open for some years until, when the angry Austrians were appeased, and the University of Pavia reopened its doors, it became again a simple hospital. Since then—the second half of the nineteenth century—surgical activity has abated at the Istituto. Was this the fault of politics, or of less definable reasons? The truth is that after the glorious school of the Moscati, of Monteggia, and of Palletta, the Università Medica Ospedaliera fell into a sleep, and the operative art entered a transitional period, in fact, fell into a decline.

The old technique had given all that its means allowed; new surgical methods had to arise; it was the epoch of the great bacteriological discoveries, of testing various antiseptic methods. Lister's discoveries found at the hospital more skeptics than believers, and the skeptics (quite naturally) were mainly the old general surgeons on the staff. These, while glorying in the achievements of the past, had reached an age where it is human to reject all novelty, an age when one doubts more than one hopes. Surprised and beaten they might be: convinced they were not.

So, while Pavia had its Bottini, Paris its Péan, Berlin its Langenbeck, Vienna its Billroth, and Geneva its Reverdin, Milan had none who could be compared to these giants. This was when I arrived at the Central Hospital. Though it hurt, I had to face the harsh truth.

Surgery had developed, centuries ago, in those old halls. The septic and aseptic patients lay side by side, and the operations almost always took place in these wards. When they had to perform an important operation—an amputation or a disarticulation—a messenger was sent through the hospital to inform the other doctors, as though it were an extraordinary event, and the operation took place in the notorious Palletta operating theater, where everything was right for anything except aseptic surgery.

I do not speak of methods of clinical investigation, or of laboratory research, or of sepsis or antisepsis. To give an idea of this surgical Boeotia, I will recall a classic incident which, if not precisely true, is significant from the mere fact of its currency. They say that a surgeon, who gave a course in anatomy, was accustomed, without washing himself, and with his nails and cuticle still filthy with the blood of the cadavers, to operate on, and dress, his poor patients.

Then there is the story of another surgeon who was performing a Caesarian section—with the fission of the uterine peduncle to the abdominal walls—when he saw that the assistants had forgotten a rubber seton. Without bothering, he turned toward a window, cut off part of the cord, and used it to bind up the uterine stalk.

Some of the surgeons just did not know what they were about. One, about to operate on an abscess in the neck, exclaimed: "What the devil is this! God alone knows!"

The knife lost its way in the carotid regions, so the poor patient went to heaven rather prematurely.

Some of these fine fellows were noted for their impulsiveness and obstinacy. Take the case of the poor fellow who was waiting to be operated on for a scrotal strangulated hernia. The assistants knew all about the case, and had made all the necessary preparations. The professor arrived, and began to contradict his assistants, making a contrary diagnosis, and asserting that it was a common hydrocele, and not a hernia at all. Without waiting, with no preparation at all, he seized the trocar and plunged it in the scrotal region. . . . Gas and fecal matter poured out. The rest can be left to the imagination.

These and many other episodes about which I remain discreetly silent are often told to give an idea of the scientific and technical state of the surgical art in this ill-omened period. Fortunately, things were going to change, thanks especially to two famous personages: Mangiagalli, in gynecology, and Dalle Ore, in general surgery.

Mangiagalli lit into the old methods with a vengeance. Prejudice, skepticism, and superstition were banished in one fell swoop. He introduced the most scrupulous antisepsis, and loudly declared that laparotomy, if performed under optimum conditions, was safe. Ten years later, when he was unanimously named professor at Pavia, he devoted his inaugural address to his own laparotomical labors, and stunned his audience. He passed for a fantastic dreamer, but the laparotomical operations of which he spoke had actually been performed at the Central Hospital, and it was to the Istituto's credit that it had allowed Mangiagalli to test out his technique there.

What Mangiagalli did in gynecology, Dalle Ore matched

in general surgery. Better hospital quarters were the reward of his brilliant efforts. Surgery left the old buildings for the fine new buildings, with their superb equipment. Thanks again to Mangiagalli, the graduate surgical clinics were opened, and these competed with the new university. The encouragement that the Central Hospital gave to these institutions is simply enormous. The hospital itself furnished the larger part of the clinical material, and it is no exaggeration to say that the university could not have existed without the hospital.

So the dream of Moscati and Verga came true after many long years. The old hospital schools had outdistanced the University of Milan. What had been called Boeotia only a few years before was now the admitted center of study in northern Italy: *Universitas studiorum.* On the site of Francesco Sforza's old villa rose the greatest institute of pathological anatomy in the world. The hospital furnished not only buildings and schools, but the masters, also.

Many of the leading staff surgeons were deemed worthy of a chair, and, after a regular competition, were elected professors. In surgery there was no one, at first, from another university. All had matured at the hospital, and the first director of the surgical clinic was Professor Baldo Rossi, head surgeon of the Zonda pavilion. The first professor of surgical pathology was Professor Castiglioni, head surgeon of the Ponti pavilion. I, head surgeon of the Moscati pavilion, was professor of symptomatic surgery. The professor of operative medicine was Professor Crosti, then Professor Bagozzi, both head surgeons of the Litta pavilion.

So there came into being a Milanese school of surgery, which carried on the glorious traditions of the past.

Chapter VII

ON MY TRAVELS

Adieu, adieu! my native shore
Fades o'er the waters blue;
The night-winds sigh, the breakers roar;
And shrieks the wild sea-mew.
                    —Byron: *Childe Harold's Pilgrimage*

AS I STOOD ALONE AT THE STERN, AND WATCHED THE PORT
and city of Genoa fade in the distance, I thought of these
verses by Byron, which I had salvaged from my youthful
studies. The steamer *Duca di Genova*, bounding over the
high seas, would not touch land before reaching New York.
I was going to cross the ocean for the first time, and I
almost felt frightened as I faced the unknown.

It was a gloomy evening, much like that described in
Childe Harold's Pilgrimage: a February evening favorable
to solitude and meditation. I could not tear myself away
from the rail: I was watching my native land, thinking
of the last two years during which I had given myself
up selflessly to surgery. Henceforth surgery was to be my
life: it was my chosen career.

By rigid economy I had been able, during my six years
of work, to abandon my practice almost completely, and
give myself over to my studies. By chance I was brought in
contact with Professor Baldo Rossi, the recently appointed
head surgeon, and I had volunteered my assistance at the
Ponti pavilion. There I had put the laboratory in order,

and made an inventory of all the apparatus and material. Not satisfied with this purely clinical and operative task, I had carried on exacting scientific and experimental researches at the Institute of Serotherapeutics in Milan, where Professor Belfanti and Professor Ascoli welcomed and supported me. Thanks to these friendly savants I was able to finish a series of studies that I developed in my experimental work on opsonin and on the prognosis of abdominal wounds.

At the end of 1908, after two years of severe mental labor and physical weariness (which seemed almost negligible, since I was at last on the track of my ideal), I had the satisfaction of winning the Parravicini Prize: a generous scholarship that would allow me a long journey and residence abroad, where I could acquire further knowledge and experience of certain branches of medicine. That year the competition had been up my special alley: surgery of the digestive tract, and its improvement—a problem of peculiar interest to me. I entered the lists enthusiastically, and the results, singling me out from among so many talented contestants, had been most gratifying. I could devote myself wholly to science without thinking about money or professional engagements.

I left January 1, 1909.

Lausanne was my first stop: a charming town in spring and summer, but hateful in winter, full of wild and mysterious Russian students of both sexes. I halted, drawn there by the fame of Roux and his clinic. Thence I went to other Swiss universities noted for their surgical achievements—Geneva and Professor Girard, Berne and Dr. Kocher. Great names, now almost forgotten.

I was already disillusioned in two months, and was about

to entrain for Berlin when I met a very congenial observer, Dr. Doederlein, of Chicago. Like myself, he was on a self-improvement tour, and had chosen Europe. He told me that any self-respecting American surgeon had to go abroad before practising. It was the rule, no matter whether the trip lasted a year or two weeks—he had to breathe European air, even if it were only the air of Parisian cafés or Berlin beerhalls. Having been to Europe was the important thing.

Despite his flippant moments, Doederlein was essentially a serious man. He went frequently to the clinics, was present at the operations, and was unsparing in his acute criticisms. He bewailed the fact that so many Americans went to Europe, and so few Europeans either knew nothing of American surgery or held it in contempt. "We have gone to your glorious schools," he told me, "and we have applied what we learned there—applied it on a vast scale and with the help of vast endowments. In your own field—abdominal surgery—don't forget the Americans. There you will find brilliant laparotomists, impressive statistics, inspired methods. . . ."

Gradually I came to a decision: I would take Doederlein's tip. I said good-by to Switzerland, rushed back to Milan to pack, and booked passage on the first boat.

As I hung over the rail, watching Genoa fade in the distance, I thought of Doederlein's words, of the itinerary he had mapped out for me, of his words of good cheer.

The crossing was horrible.

Bad weather descended on us in the Gulf of Lyons, and followed us practically into New York: twelve days of hell, the worst of which came right in middle of the Atlantic. March 9, 1909, will remain engraved on my memory like a day of wrath. The boat groaned as though it were going to break in two any minute. It was impossible to stand up, equally so to sit down: everything was topsy-turvy. There were four of us in the dining salon that day; the others had retired to their cabins. The captain was anything but chipper. He stood on the navigating bridge, and did not trust himself to leave it a minute.

Finally the sea quieted down, and through the fog we saw the flat coast of America: Sandy Hook, the sentinel of the Hudson. Scarcely had we entered the still waters of the estuary when the boat was repeopled, as if by magic. A crowd of passengers poured from the cabins, and swarmed over the deck—exhausted creatures, staring hungrily at land, who had not stirred from their cabins since we had left Genoa.

They told me that three thousand immigrants were traveling steerage. I had seen them only once, and then by chance. Off the Azores, one evening, I was going to my cabin when I was accosted by the ship's doctor, who asked me to accompany him to the sick ward. I staggered below (the tempest was at the height of its fury), and was taken to see a man, possibly forty years old or so, half naked and covered with blood, whom the ship's doctor and the government agent were examining. When I appeared, they asked me to help them, and share their responsibilities.

During a dispute that had flared up, a couple of emigrants, probably so they would not get out of practice, had gone at each other with knives. The poor wretch in the sick ward had been stabbed in the abdomen. He was slightly wounded in the left flank. Possibly the knife had pierced the intestine, though it was not certain.

What could be done? The problem worried the ship's doctor. We looked at each other, and understood each other without speaking.

If we had been in a decent clinic, with an ample and experienced staff, the answer would have been simple: an exploratory laparotomy, working down, layer by layer. But in this primitive first-aid station, amid this rolling and pitching, it would be rash to try a laparotomy. I advised watchful waiting, though of course the wound had first to be disinfected.

Fortunately there were no complications, and forty-eight hours later the three of us breathed a sigh of relief: myself, the ship's doctor, and the wounded man. Another person was also well pleased—the impetuous Calabrian who had struck the blow, and who, according to rules on shipboard, should have been put in irons and delivered over to the proper authorities. As a matter of fact, he got off cheaply, because the wounded man was already up and about when we reached New York. The captain neglected to report the case, and the lesion, which might have uncovered the crime, escaped the scrutiny of the American authorities.

Had we made the exploratory laparotomy (as, strictly speaking, was our duty), the business would have ended differently.

Meanwhile the *Duca di Genova* slowly steamed through the Hudson estuary toward the gigantic metropolis. It was raining. In the excitement of landing so close at hand, those three thousand emigrants, whom I had seen in the hold—the men pale and emaciated, the women weary after the long passage—began rushing up the stairs and pouring through the doors. With their miserable packs at their backs, they looked like ghosts disgorged from the bowels of the ship. Some of the women were nursing wizened babies at their breasts. They were headed toward the unknown, in quest of a fortune that would probably elude them.

The huge statue of Liberty rose through the fog, and the vague outlines of the great skyscrapers were just perceptible through the heavy smoke. The infernal din of a great port filled the air. The *Duca di Genova* docked neatly at one of the numerous piers, that of the Navigazione Generale Italiana: the Italian Lines.

New York, the world city, a veritable maelstrom of peoples, seems at first sight like a gigantic monstrosity: a very bad impression to make on an Italian full of traditional ideas about beauty and art. Those insolent skyscrapers and the noisy clang of the "El" are amazing, but scarcely admirable. It is worse still if the unforeseen spectacle greets your eyes some March morning, and you already are cursing the light but chilling downpour. I left the boat with an engineer from Turin, and as we walked to the hotel I felt that our thoughts were the same every time our glances met. We saw in our mind's eye our small but delightful Italian cities, with their elegant buildings and spacious squares, as we had seen them, drenched with Italy's incomparable sunlight.

This does not mean I was tempted to go back home at once. I had come to America on a scientific mission, not on a pleasure trip, and on that score I had no complaints to make. America was better than I had imagined. I gave up asking for what America could not give, and concentrated on the practical and useful. I was truly amazed at the magnificent scientific and commercial enterprises—testifying to native boldness and organizing genius.

My first lesson in American ingenuity: the enormous hotels, that are as self-sufficing as a small city. I lived at my hotel for weeks at a time without making purchases elsewhere. On the ground floor or lower levels are all sorts of shops and offices: laundries, candy stores, haberdashers, hairdressers, manicurists, shoe stores and shoe-shining establishments, bars, concert halls, theaters, and cinemas. On the first floors are lecture halls, smoking rooms, reception rooms, writing rooms, and on the higher floors are the bedrooms and apartments. Higher still are the terraces and roof gardens, and, at the very top, observatories for panoramic views.

In America, the hotel is, in a sense, public domain. At any rate, the rooms on the ground floors are open to all. A continual stream of people, never questioned about their business, never obliged to make any purchase, can go in, and do whatever they like: rest, read the newspapers, write letters, or merely look at the crowd.

Admirable as are the hotels, equally so are many other public or private institutions: railroad stations, post offices, schools, and, particularly, hospitals. All these institutions are superbly organized.

The first hospital I chanced to inspect was Mount Sinai, a Jewish institution located in the heart of the city. It is a model of luxury, cleanliness, and order. A spacious, columned vestibule intervenes between the main entrance and the administrative offices. The private rooms and wards are on the intermediate floors, and the laboratories and operating rooms are above these. The many floors are served by a large number of elevators. The sick rooms are furnished luxuriously; the floors are hardwood, the walls plastered. The place is filled with flowers, and everything is white, shining, spotlessly clean. I began to compare this with certain old rooms which, despite the care they receive daily, always seem dusty.

But the luxury surpasses itself in the operating rooms. Those of the Mount Sinai Hospital are veritable amphitheaters of marble and crystal, stocked with every possible scientific necessity. In the various wards, laboratories, study rooms, all is done silently, almost automatically, so quickly and cleverly is the work divided among, and executed by, the doctors, assistants, and attendants. The white uniformed nurses, however, strike the most characteristic note in this splendid institution.

The organization and scrupulous division of labor are basic features of every truly American institution. Hotels, hospitals, public offices, warehouses—all work toward the same end: avoiding as much as possible the weakening and separation of resources and means. All function in the same way. The same working methods obtain at the Rockefeller Institute for Medical Research as at the Baldwin Locomotive Works at Philadelphia, the Chicago Stockyards, and St. Mary's Hospital at Rochester.

See what happens, for example, in the gigantic Stockyards, the central Chicago slaughterhouse (or, at least, what happened when I visited it).

The poor cattle were slaughtered and dismembered *en série*. They entered the death chamber by a door, and as they entered a specialist gave them a knockout blow. Then they were hooked by the tendon of Achilles on to a moving chain which passed in front of a line of a hundred butchers. Each specialist had but a single operation to perform as the carcass passed by. For example, one detached the horns, another the hoofs, another the ears. When the hook had passed the last butcher, there was nothing left of the cow: she had been dismembered piecemeal, and all the pieces had fallen through the floor traps to the basements where they underwent further treatment.

Needless to say, each of the experts did his share perfectly, for he had never done anything else, and he would not have been able to do his job if he had been another kind of expert. So workmen exist today who have never done anything, or thought of doing anything, except cutting off horns, or hoofs, or ears, as the case may be. Superb organization and perfect division of labor, no doubt, but the man who narrows his daily perspective down to this single task—this rigidly prescribed bit of manual labor—ends by becoming little more than a cretin.

It is easy to find analogies in all the industrial establishments, in the workshops or laboratory: from the Chicago Stockyards to the Baldwin works, from the Ford factories to the Wanamaker warehouses. The most curious part of it is that the system can be applied to the most noble manifestations of human activity—to surgery, for example. The clinic of the Mayo Brothers at Rochester, Minnesota, proves my case.

The Mayo clinic was, at this time, the Mecca of surgery, and all the leading American physicians and surgeons had made the pilgrimage one time or another. The most miraculous operations were performed there, and there they compiled the most impressive statistics. The two Mayos directed it. They had literally created it out of nothing, modeling it after an industrial establishment, after a modern factory, in fact. Thus the patient who wishes to be treated at the Mayo clinic must present his credentials at the registration bureau, which includes a number of waiting rooms, a certain number of offices, and a no less greater number of consultation rooms. In each office is a specialist who examines only the patients who come within his special province.

The patient returns to the main office where he receives a divisional card. After a brief interrogation a nurse finds out the disease in question, or rather, what is the diseased organ, and sends the patient to the office assigned to such cases. The specialist examines him, questions him, and, whenever necessary, confers with other specialists (the X-ray expert, the chemist, the histologist), and finally, if the patient needs an operation, hands him over to the surgeon or, more precisely, to the operator. The latter sees the patient on the operating table, and consults the diagnosis: it is admirably presented and painstaking in detail. In other words, the operator has his task planned for him in advance. He has only to take up the surgical knife, and cut.

Needless to say, the division of labor was carried straight through to the operating room, and each operator had his specialty. I recall that William Mayo preferred the abdomen, Charles Mayo the head and neck, etc.

By means of such admirable organization and division of labor, preordained, thorough and carried to incredible lengths, the Mayos got results that no single independent surgeon had ever been able to obtain. All this is very good. But when one thinks that the doctors, all their life, do only one thing, more or less circumscribed—the anesthetizers, for example, who only administer ether, and so on—one thinks again (such is the insidious association of ideas) of the Armour and Company butchers in Chicago, of those expert amputators of horns, hoofs, and ears, good fellows all, but who, outside of their little specialty, can do nothing else.

The Latin temperament revolts against this restriction of personal activity, and reserves its admiration for the great universal geniuses, men like Leonardo, Michelangelo, Pico della Mirandola, and, in medicine, for the great synthetic minds, the inspired clinicians, noteworthy for their general culture and naturally disposed to a many-sided activity.

The Americans and their disciples will say that I am mistaken, but my Latin temperament would never permit me to think that one-sidedness can, in itself, compare with the rich and fruitful intuitions that are native to universal minds.

Although I did not feel thoroughly convinced by the tendency in American surgery, I could but acknowledge the vast strides they had made in operative technique. I met few outstanding clinicians on my tour, but I found many brilliant operators—at Chicago, Philadelphia, Baltimore, New York.

American surgeons are noted for their skill, the operating rooms are perfect, the work is admirably distributed: I often was present at operations when not a single word was spoken. In abdominal operations the most exquisite care is observed: the sutures resemble fine embroidery, the asepsis is flawless, general and local anesthesia are administered perfectly, and the instrument case is complete down to the veriest minutiae. I recall that certain nurses do nothing except prepare the materials for the sutures, and these materials, too, offer an endless variety in quality and modes of preparation.

Such scrupulous attention to detail did not leave me unmoved. With an ever growing interest in every novelty I saw I passed from the clinics and hospitals of New York to those of Chicago, Rochester, Baltimore, and Philadelphia. Back in New York, I decided to end my stay in the United States by observing Carrel's work at the Rockefeller Institute: both his transplantation of organs and glands—a new departure—and his operations on blood vessels. I would be unjust to a great country, and to the fine surgeons who generously revealed their marvels, if I did not acknowledge gratefully all the benefits I received in the United States. But I must admit that I left this land of miracles without much regret.

I left toward the first of May aboard the *Adriatic*, one of the giant steamers of the White Star Line. From the quarterdeck I saw that forest of skyscrapers, at the tip of Manhattan, disappear, then Brooklyn and the huge statue of Liberty, and then the peninsula of Sandy Hook, the last stretch of visible land . . . and I turned my back on the new world without a sigh. The sight of so many marvels had dazzled my eyes, and filled my mind, but nothing (or very little) had touched my heart. America was no place for me. Every day I felt, more and more, a nostalgia for Europe, especially for Italy.

The men so taken up with business and so fond of gold had not won me completely. They were accustomed to judge the worth of others in money. *"How much is that fellow worth?"* (It is only too true that money is the measure of everything in this world.) And the women did not please me overmuch. True, they were often very lovely and full of life, but they were too patently given over to pleasure, often too unfeeling, too accustomed to

think of their husbands simply as ministers to their vanity
and taste for luxury. Further, the young men displeased
me. I must admit that these robust fellows were well prepared to fight both the battle of sport and the battle of life,
but they were too ready to leave their parents, and forget
them in the interests of money and social standing. As for
the cities, it is enough to mention that they are monotonous
in their uninspired symmetry, and are totally lacking in
artistic interest. Moreover, they lack the warmth of my beloved Europe—and Italy.

After six days on the water, on my way from Cherbourg
to Paris, I felt that I had awakened from a dream, and
awakened near to home. It was a lovely May morning, and
the sun was shining brightly, when I saw the Champs-
Élysées and the Louvre. I greeted the Seine and the
Invalides with the friendliness I felt for these old comrades. . . . I cannot express as clearly as I feel that sensation that many other Italians must have felt. It is that no
matter what the historical and geographical distance between them, it seems that Paris has never been very far
from Milan.

When finally, forty-eight hours later, I saw the pinnacles of the cathedral and the golden Madonnina, I began
to cry like a child. I was in my own country again. I was
home. May I live there until I die.

My family awaited me at the barrier in the old central
station. Mamma was in tears, my sister was moved, my
brother was gloomy and preoccupied. My absence had sad-
dened them, and the thought that I was going away again

for six months vexed them still more. I consoled them, and
a fortnight later I set out again for foreign parts.

First, however, Professor Mangiagalli invited me to lecture on surgery in America. The subject so appealed to
doctors that an enormous crowd poured into the vast and
imposing amphitheater in the Via Commenda—all to hear
my story. When I showed some stereopticon slides of the
great American institutes, hospitals, and universities and
their admirable methods, and ended by comparing Carrel's
remarkable experiments to the beautiful legend of Saints
Cosmas and Damian,* thunderous and prolonged applause
greeted my effort. Even today, some of my colleagues
speak warmly of my début as a public speaker. Further, I
became a public darling, and got my paragraph among the
news of the day.

In the meantime I asked permission to enter the competition for the fellowship in clinical surgery, and I had chosen
for my thesis renal haematuria, a highly timely subject, for
they were just beginning to speak of essential haematuria.
But the only writers who had made experiments in the mat-

---

* Jacobus a Voragine says that the caretaker of the old basilica of
Saint Cosmas and Damian at Rome had a leg that was half eaten away
by cancer. One night, while he was sleeping, the two saints appeared
at his bedside, and held a consultation.

"We'll have to amputate," Saint Cosmas declared, "but where can we
find a healthy leg to replace it with?"

"I have an idea," Saint Damian replied readily (for he was the patron
saint of surgeons). "They buried a man today in the cemetery of San
Pietro in Vinculis. Let us take one of his legs, and give it to our
servant."

The two saints did so. They took the dead man's leg, and grafted it
to the stump. The caretaker awakened, found himself cured, and told
everyone the story of his dream. They rushed to the grave, and it was
true—one of the legs had disappeared. In its place they found the caretaker's.

The first transplantation was commemorated by Fra Angelico in a
painting at the Museo di San Marco, Florence.

ter were Albarran, at Paris, and Israel. Unhappily Albarran had been stricken by the cruel disease that was to prove his death, so I went to Berlin.

My best friend, Aliprandi, like myself in Berlin on a scientific mission (he was studying the pathology of the digestive apparatus), was waiting for me at the Anhalt Bahnhof. He had reserved a room for me at the Pension Charité, where I found more Italian confreres, among them Professor Ferrata, the future renowned clinician of the University of Pavia, but then a simple doctor, following with brilliant comprehension the hematological lectures of the celebrated Pappenheim.

I divided my time between the Juden-Spital where Israel taught, and the Langenbeck-Haus, where Bier lectured. Our long day's work ended at evening in a café in the Alexanderplatz, where we engaged in endless scientific discussions. It seemed that we wished to exhaust the science of the great Berliners, and carry the spoils to Italy.

Berlin was at the height of its fame. Never was the might of Germany so obvious: the great capital aspired to be considered the new Athens of the entire world. The scientific institutions, the libraries, the clinics swarmed with students of all nationalities. Even Americans, Japanese, Chinese, and Indians thronged the halls of the university: a veritable pilgrimage shared by students of all nations.

The professors basked in this fame, and sometimes they seemed to look down complacently from their Olympian heights. Both Koerte, at the Krankenhaus am Urban, and Krause, at the Augusta-Spital, received me with disdainful condescension. These princes of German surgery (we were still allied, by the way) scarcely troubled to conceal the fact that Germany was *caput mundi*, that anything scientific produced outside their country simply did not exist, and that we had only to follow docilely in their footsteps, and shut up.

The Berlin libraries possessed scarcely a single Italian surgical journal. In noting this lack, I thought of our own libraries groaning with *Archiven, Zeitschriften, Centralblätter,* etc. Some of my colleagues, in order to bring their works to the attention of Italian students, were accustomed to publish their articles in German periodicals.

Still more impressive was the politico-military aspect of Berlin at the time. The great capital, like a barracks full to overflowing, practically burst with militarism. Even the scientists, even the surgeons struck military poses, and walked like soldiers. The operating garb aped the officer's cloak, hospital discipline smacked of the barracks. When my companions in exile and I went, in our leisure, to the Tempelhofer-Feld, and chanced to witness one of the frequent military parades, we had the sense to keep silent. Silently we exchanged glances, and thought of the tragic conflict that was coming.

This was in 1909: the catastrophe came five years later.

Despite this unfriendly atmosphere, despite the overripe atmosphere of Teutonic triumph, my sojourn at Berlin was not unpleasant, and I profited by it. I divided my days between the library, the Juden-Spital, and Professor Israel's house. I worked hard at my thesis on renal haematuria, and to help me the good Israel furnished me with clinical examples, suggestions, and aid. I shall never cease to revere the memory of this good, learned, and gifted man. He was, in every sense, a lovable person, though for many, alas! only a Jew. As such he had never been able (because of restrictions suffered by Jews) to attain the professoriate, of which he was so eminently worthy. All his work was carried out at the modest Juden-Spital, and yet his recognized merit had brought him to the top of the profession, and he was admittedly one of the foremost urologists of his time. Honor to him!

Chapter VIII

ROSES

At the beginning of 1910, my foreign travels ended, and with them my self-imposed task of visiting the best clinics in the world. I returned home with a treasure of methods, tendencies, and all the novelties known in the field of surgery. Saturated with science and experience, I naturally hoped that practice would seem easier, and that my position would be more secure.

I was wrong. My surgical débuts were far from easy. After a year's absence I had lost my first band of faithful—they had gone elsewhere. Furthermore, I no longer wanted to be a mere obstetrician. My former obstetrical clients no longer returned to me since I forsook the specialty. Henceforth I intended to devote myself exclusively to general surgery. Unfortunately, however, surgical work did not come my way.

I had not yet enough authority to push myself as an operator. So my pocketbook remained empty, and my morale began to weaken. To add further to my depression some of my colleagues at the hospital received me very churlishly. My words were received diffidently, the novelties considered unfavorably, skeptically. Possibly they saw me as a rival, nothing else. They smiled at me nastily, and nicknamed me . . . the American.

"You doubtless thought," my friend Bandini, to whom

complained, said drily, "that patients would meet you at the station. Be patient, and serve your apprenticeship. Your turn will come."

My good friend, who always has the sense to dish out his good advice with a laugh, was right. It so happened that the competition for the professoriate was impending. During my travels abroad I had kept on working. My thesis was ready, and bore Professor Israel's stamp of approval. I felt that the examinations would be easy for me.

The practical test, held in the small lecture hall of the old clinic of the University of Parma, filled with students, sensation-seekers, assistants, and even professors, had the following problem: "Symptoms and diagnoses of intestinal tumors." Several of my colleagues, their faces dark with suspicion, if not with hostility, had come from Milan for the occasion. They would be critical rather than indulgent, that was certain. The examiners were not very friendly, either. And they were right. What the deuce! Who was this hospital upstart who dared to try for a professoriate in clinical surgery and operative medicine without passing through the university apprenticeship? He must have a nerve. . . . Wasn't the clinical professoriate reserved for the university aides, and furthermore, could one hold it without having first held that of pathology?

In the eyes of my enemies I passed for one of those practitioners who want the title of professor only for its effect, commercially speaking, on their visiting cards. To these one should be severe, and therefore the examiners scowled at me. I was unknown in university circles, and I was a beginner.

I began stammering, almost tremulously. But when I got started on this very important division of clinical surgery, words came easily. Everything I had learned in a hard year's work came back, and I had the satisfaction of seeing the attentive faces become less suspicious, less unfriendly: they actually looked kindly and not a little amazed. At the end of the allotted hour the president signed time up, and the roof rang with loud and prolonged applause. The good Baldo Rossi warmly wrung my hand and embraced me. Castiglione was visibly moved, and all crowded around to shake my hand.

I returned to Milan . . . I will not say triumphant . . . but satisfied. And—it wasn't so strange, was it?—I began to get patients.

So began the better part of my professional life—what the Germans call *werden*: not being, but becoming, progressing, aspiring. My old friends at the Obstetrical Station were my principal assistants and colleagues. They named me consulting surgeon of the clinic they had founded, the Asilo Regina Elena, and that famous institution, then so small and obscure, was the first theater of my operating technique.

When I began my career, surgery was, as I have said, at its height.

With anesthesia perfected, asepsis improved by the adoption of the large sterilizers, rubber gloves, sterilized thread, and the finest and most delicate apparatus, surgeons had invented all the methods they could imagine.

"*Ce fut un monde nouveau que cette chirurgie moderne,*" to cite Faure, "*qui avait dépassé tous les rêves et accompli tous les miracles, et dans sa partie technique était arrivée si haut, qu'il est presque permis de dire, qu'elle ne pouvait plus que descendre. . . .*" In fact, since then technique has (at least, in its larger aspects) progressed but little. There are some changes in detail, but the main outlines are the same, with one notable difference: then enthusiasm knew no bounds, boldness did not stop this side of temerity; today we are more calm, more cautious, sometimes incredibly so.

In such an atmosphere of warm enthusiasm, my début was exceptionally happy. Thoughts of one of my first operations still move me. One day I was resting when a man, about fifty years old, was ushered in: a man who seemed to be suffering acutely. He looked thoroughly depressed, like a person tired of life, and ready for anything, even suicide. He handed me a letter from a colleague in Lugano, and there I read that he was suffering from chronic neuralgia of the trigeminal nerve. The patient had been suffering, off and on, for several years. The pains, beginning in the region of the eye and forehead, spread to the right side of the head and face. The maddening pain faded after a few hours, only to recur soon again with renewed intensity.

The poor devil had tried every possible remedy. He had visited all the Swiss universities, he had tried all the cures, including local injections of alcohol, but all in vain. I examined him, and found that the two most painful nerves were the sub- and supraorbital. Checked at their point of departure, they caused veritable spasms of agony. I advised extirpating these sub- and supraorbital canals without delay. The very simple and safe operation was performed almost immediately in my office, with the most favorable results. The poor fellow went home, happy and triumphant: his pains had disappeared.

I was six months without news of him, and then one day, during consulting hours, my houseman came to say that he had admitted a patient who, after saying that he wished to speak with me, had fallen, groaning and twisting, to the floor. I rushed to the poor wretch, who was squealing like a dog, and laid him on the couch: I waited for the attack to pass. Then he told me his sad story. He had returned to Lugano, happy to resume his daily life in the bosom of his family—for his pains had really disappeared. Five months later they began again, worse than before, because they were more violent and more frequent, making work impossible.

He was a devout man, and he had a wife and eleven children: but he could no longer live that way. He had hitherto steeled himself against suicide. I realized that he was almost at the end of his tether, but had returned to me as a last resort. He asked me to use the boldest expedients to save him. He sobbed, wrung his hands, even kneeled and flung himself on the floor. I looked on, quite bewildered. Never, in my brief career, had I witnessed such extremity of despair. What could I do for the poor wretch?

Something had to be done. The peripheral region having failed, I had to turn to the endocranium; that is, I had to open the cranial box, trace the trigeminal nerve to its source, and kill the Gasserian ganglion, which receives all the branches of this nerve.*

It's easy enough to say. Actually, I shuddered at the thought of performing such a risky operation. I had a wonderful book knowledge of this operation, but I had performed it only on cadavers. It was said that someone in Milan had tried it, but the results of the operation had not been published. It almost seemed folly for a mere beginner to try it—and on a private patient, too. On the other hand,

---

* Now they do not extract the ganglion, for the so-called retro-Gasserian neurotomy is much easier and is less unpleasant.

I had not the heart to refuse—I had to proceed. . . . The sufferer had paused in his contortions. He looked at me, and read my thoughts. He took my hands in his: "Try anything," he pled. "I have faith in you. Even if you kill me, it will be better than feeling remorse for letting me kill myself. If you are afraid, I will give you a signed authorization."

I smiled, for I was thinking of this very necessity. And he wrote and signed a statement whose elaborate details freed me from any responsibility as to the outcome of the operation.

So, two days later, the operation was performed in the presence of the doctor from Lugano and of my many eager but trembling assistants: the Gasserian ganglion was extracted, and the sufferer, cured and happy, was present, nineteen days later, at the Society of Medicine and Biology.

I recall my colleagues' disbelief. Good old Professor Denti even wanted to touch the patient's cornea, to see whether feeling had really been destroyed. When I showed him the fine Gasserian ganglion, thoroughly intact, in the vessel, even some of my best friends said that it was too nearly perfect, and that it had been taken from a cadaver. Fortunately there had been many witnesses to the operation, and the best proof, of course, was the happiness of my patient, cured—this time—forever.

Signora Ermellina is now a charming matron who looks after her ever growing and thriving brood. But when I first knew her, at the beginning of my career, the lady was neither married nor healthy: she was merely a delicate girl in alarmingly poor health.

She came to me because she had lost her faith in medicine,

and had heard that surgery works miracles. She suffered from abdominal troubles that none had been able to explain, much less treat and cure: intermittent stomach-ache, bad digestion, stubborn constipation, occasional diarrhea, and constant pain. This had been going on for more than a year. Doctors who had examined her were vague in their symptomatology: one had suggested colitis, another appendicitis. Recently a swelling had appeared on the right side, and then certain doctors suggested a floating kidney. It was a hopeless mess.

At an age when life should have been especially lovely, the poor girl despaired. Her life was an endless agony, and she had turned to surgery in her desperation. She was ready—so she said—to be cured, or killed in one fell stroke: death was better than such a life.

She looked at me with her blue eyes, moist and pleading. How could I help but be moved?

After carefully studying the case, and after many examinations I concluded that the girl's intestine was severely injured, in some places shrunk and obstructed. But the nature and cause of the disease remained doubtful, for none of the various chemical, microscopic, and X-ray tests had infallibly pointed to a solution of the problem. I promised the young woman only one thing—to use all the resources of the operative art. With the patient's consent I opened the abdomen, and found there just what I feared: a tuberculosis along a considerable segment of the intestine. Certain portions were shrunk and obstructed, others were distended so as to resemble tumors. I had to remove all the diseased part: a good portion of the small intestine, all the caecum with the appendix, all the ascending colon, and a large part of the transverse colon—more than a yard in all.

The diseased parts cut away, I joined the end of the small colon to the extremity of the transverse colon, and the operation was finished. A fortnight later the patient was able to leave the hospital, and soon she felt completely cured. Of her pains there remained but a memory. After a few weeks, she began to flower once more . . . and then I lost sight of her.

I heard a bit later that she was engaged, and one fine day I met her at the arcade, on the arm of her fiancé. She saw me, smiled, but did not stop. Possibly I recalled too many sad memories; possibly she feared that I would reveal details that had better be forgotten, and of which her fiancé knew nothing.

Anyhow, I felt proud in having contributed to her very evident happiness.

In surgery there are certain cases that put to a hard test the clinician's judgment and the operator's capacity—terribly difficult cases, fiendishly complicated, fraught with vexation. The treatment is toilsome, and yet crowned with success. The layman knows nothing of these cases, nor can he properly appreciate them. On the other hand, there are brilliant cases, involving an easy operation and simple treatment, which astound the lay public, although we naturally consider them absurdly easy. The public remains indifferent to a villainous cerebral tumor or to the removal of a pyloric cancer, but goes into ecstasies if the surgeon leaves the operating theater with an enormous ovarian cyst or a uterine tumor that fills a whole washbasin.

In reality there are some operations which are done easily, though the results are impressive, and there are others which make a surgeon's reputation, and which bring a numerous clientele to his door. At the beginning of my career I had several such cases.

Take the case of the colonel's lady. That, if you wish, redounded greatly to my credit. The poor woman did not know what good digestion meant, and the nutritive function was, to her, merely a synonym for hell. Every meal was a source of anxiety, for after it was over, especially if she had eaten highly seasoned food, she suffered the most intense pain in the epigastric region, "at the mouth of the stomach," as she explained it. These torments sometimes lasted for several hours; then they faded away and disappeared. At first, since the unpleasantness had begun shortly after her marriage, she had given it little attention, but the pains soon became all-absorbing. She felt as though a sword were piercing her stomach. The poor woman got into the habit of retiring, after the meal, to her bedroom, where she rolled in agony on her bed. Groaning, she held her stomach. . . .

Cramps in the stomach, acidity heightened by gastric juice, gastric ulcer: all had been suggested and discussed. Her first pregnancy had intensified her trouble, and she had not been able to suckle her baby. However, after her delivery, she submitted to a severe regimen, and that, together with long and elaborate medicinal treatment, had resulted, little by little, in the complete disappearance of the pains.

Some years later the gastric disturbances reappeared. The acute pain no longer followed each meal; rather, the patient felt no pain, but when she ate, she felt definitely that she was not digesting. *The food did not pass.* After eating she felt a weight on her stomach, as though the food had been stopped stubbornly on the way, and sometimes, some hours later, she belched. The eructation was acid, painful, embarrassing. More physicians and specialists were consulted, and then began the long agony of various treatments, all of which were useless. The poor woman's sufferings were wearisome both to herself and her family. Eating had become a torture, and if she could have stopped, she would have done so willingly. In the meantime she fluctuated between despair and apathy. Her beauty had vanished, her thinness was phenomenal, and her temper was uncertain.

Thus she passed many years: the most beautiful part of her life.

At last X-rays were taken, and from them it was concluded what should have seemed fairly obvious: she had an old pyloric ulcer, properly diagnosed by the family physician, and cicatrized by him. At the time, apparently, she had been cured, but the cicatrice had formed a ring, a little belt that had gradually shrunk, then obstructed the pyloric orifice. Thus food could pass from the stomach only with the greatest difficulty, and only in small bits. These were deposited all along the gastric pouch, which therefore had become more and more distended. In short, there was formed what is known scientifically as cicatrized stenosis of the pylorus, with secondary gastrectasia.

Someone had advised surgery, but the woman was afraid of instruments . . . and furthermore the family physician had advised them to think the matter over very carefully. These surgeons had a way of getting people to heaven before their time. . . . So, after wasting her youth in torments, the woman had reached maturity, and would have gone on the same way if things had not become worse. The pylorus was clogged completely, and then she vomited all she had eaten, even liquids. . . . That was the last straw.

The colonel called in a conscientious consultant who was struck speechless by so much physical misery. How had things been allowed to come to this pass, and after so many years of suffering? Call a surgeon at once—if indeed there is still time! A bold fellow is needed—a man of courage. The consultant almost shouted. He was right: it took courage to touch this living corpse.

When I had moved the woman to the hospital, I began by strengthening her with cardiotonic and hypodermic injections, for there was scarcely any pulse. When I emptied her stomach with the pump, I found remains of eggs that she had eaten more than three months before. As soon as her general condition was improved, I performed a gastroenterostomy—a quick and easy operation which aims at establishing a new, commodious means of communication between the stomach and the intestine.

Ten days later the woman left the hospital. Her trouble was over. Henceforth she could eat anything, and digest as she had never done before. She was happy, transfigured. A month later she weighed over one hundred and fifty pounds (twice her previous weight), and no one would have recognized her. Her temper, quite naturally, improved.

She invited to dinner her friends, relatives, and all those who had witnessed her misery, and sang the praises of the man who had performed the miracle they all could see. I was a savior, almost a demigod. My name traveled from drawing room to drawing room, and my clientele grew and grew. I was going to become the fashionable surgeon— all because of a simple gastroenterostomy.

There are many other brilliant cases of this sort, but I shall mention only a few which, besides their happy outcome, may have a clinical, operative, and even a scientific interest.

I was fortunate in my work on the bile ducts and the liver.

In Milan, in those days, there was very little biliary surgery, and for that little they used old and primitive methods. I had just returned from the German and American clinics, where I learned many operative details that I was eager to use. I performed many serious operations which were reported in the medical journals, while the patients were shown at scientific societies and congresses. Among my many operations on the bile ducts, I recall one which brought my name into prominence less because of the operation itself than of the quality of the patient—a noblewoman belonging to the highest Milanese society.

For a dozen years the woman had been troubled by hepatic colic. She was forty-eight years old when she felt the first pains, in the beginning months apart, then at the interval of a few weeks. She usually felt the pains after eating; they were on the right side, a little under the ribs. The pains, sometimes very severe, almost acute, rapidly became intolerable, and the patient had to lie down. But even in bed the spasms did not abate: they crept up toward the shoulder, and even extended to the back. Her regular physician always prescribed the same remedies: warm compresses on the affected parts, and injections of morphine. Despite this the suffering lasted several hours; then it faded and disappeared, leaving the whole region sore. Sometimes a slight fever, sometimes even, a few days later, a touch of jaundice. "Biliary colic," decreed the good physician, colecystitis, possibly gallstones. All remedies were tried, all spas were visited, and all mineral waters experimented with.

Nothing helped: the attacks occurred more often, and they were more violent.

Since the colic came on after meals, the poor woman no longer wished to eat, and she grew as thin as a skeleton. Her very rich husband had called a consultation of the best physicians, and they had all confirmed the diagnosis, and advised the same treatment. Not one of them advised surgery. Meanwhile, twelve years had passed, and the woman was dying. She even refused liquids, and her condition was such that she had to stay in bed. Then they first thought of calling in a surgeon. And for the first time in my life I refused to operate.

Her general condition seemed so serious to me that I did not wish to risk performing such a severe operation. I hesitated too because I thought it unfair to call me in as a last resort, particularly since failure, in view of the woman's social standing, might bring professional disaster to one so young as I. I finally yielded, however, to the prayers of the family and to the arguments of a most reputable colleague. The woman was transported by Red Cross ambulance to a private hospital, and there operated on after hurried preparations. The lesions of the bile ducts were very serious—they could not have been otherwise after so many years of suffering. The operation was a veritable battle against death, but I came out victorious.

Many years have passed since then, and I still see my patient often. Now radiant with health, she admits that she began to enjoy life only after my operation. But when I think that the same operation might have been performed, with greater ease and, above all, greater chances of success, I cannot help but deplore the hostility of certain physicians and, particularly, of the public to surgical operations.

How many sufferings would be alleviated, how many
lives saved if the patients were only turned over to the surgeon in time! But surgery is always considered the last resort, and too often we have to operate on patients *in articulo
mortis.* For this reason we sometimes fail, and our failures
are wrongly attributed to surgery. The true culprit is not
the operator, but the one who does not find, or does not
wish to find, the real symptoms, or if he does discover them,
does not wish to proceed on the basis of his findings.

Speaking of gallstones, a very noted clinician told me
frankly to call the surgeon only in case of grave complications, such as an abscess of the gall bladder or the mechanical occlusion of the bile duct. Carrying this idea to its
logical conclusion, we should operate only on strangulated
hernias, on appendices only after peritonitis has set in, on
perforated gastric ulcers. Working on this basis, our statistics would be sad, our profession an unenviable one.
Let us hope that physicians will begin to see the light, and
particularly that the public will be so educated that the
surgeon can carry on his work under more favorable conditions.

In operating I have always tried, as much as possible, not
to deform the human body. I do not mean that I perform
esthetic surgery. Effacing wrinkles, filling out facial depres-
sions, rejuvenating faded complexions, and building up
flabby breasts—that I leave to the beauticians: no serious
surgeon would give such activity a moment's thought.
Nevertheless it is proper, in fact, one is in duty bound to
think of the beauty of the members he must cut, and cut so
as to leave the smallest possible blemish.

When a four-inch incision is enough, it is useless to make an eight-inch one. Just as the incision must correspond to a natural wrinkle, so also if, thanks to a slight displacement of the tissues, the incision can be made in a region covered by hair, it would be criminal not to think of it. A good surgeon never forgets this. But esthetic considerations should never jeopardize the result of the operation. The patient's life and health come first.

The esthetic aspect is especially important in treating young girls or young women, especially if the face or throat is involved. I remember having astonished my good friend and confrere at the university when, operating on his son for a common abscess of the jaw, I constantly asked the child to smile. It is not easy to make a person who is to be operated upon smile—the invitation is a bit unseasonable. My friend could not understand my strange persistence, but when he saw that the smile had allowed me to locate the vertical wrinkle of the jaw, thus affording a natural line along which to make the incision, he was most grateful. He was even more gratified to find, later on, that the scar was hidden in the folds of the wrinkle, and was almost invisible.

Women and girls are very aware of these precautions: it is of first importance for them to hide a scar. One day a very lovely young woman came to see me, and she wept as she showed me a kind of swelling that was gradually developing on the right side of her neck. It gave her no serious trouble, neither pain nor fever, and at first it was merely a tiny button that could be easily hidden. But the button continued to grow, and became more and more visible. The family doctor suggested possibly diseased ganglia, and advised having them removed. The situation was difficult, for the young woman was engaged, and her future husband, then traveling abroad, was to return in a few weeks for the wedding. Besides the unsightliness of the mark, a scar on the throat might precipitate very natural doubts as to the health of the young woman, and entail grave consequences. The engagement might be broken off, the girl's life ruined.

The poor young creature was in despair, and rightly so: she had two or three tubercular ganglia, removable enough, accessible to nucleation, but very dangerous because they were located along the big vessels in the neck. After checking the health of the other organs, I found that these ganglia constituted her sole ailment.

My problem was to extract them so as to cure the girl before her fiancé's arrival, and yet leave neither scar nor evidence of any kind. It was hard, but I solved it. I made the incision in the hairy region of the neck, hollowing out a passage just above the large vessels. The maneuver was not easy: the operation was long and painful, it was even tricky and dangerous. At last, however, I was able to extract the group of ganglia in its entirety. The operation over, there remained only a linear scar that was hidden completely under the young woman's long and abundant hair.

No one knew of the operation, and even less of the nature of the ganglia which the miscroscope had proved to be tubercular. No one ever saw the scar, and for her fiancé Maria was always the loveliest of women. They are married, they are healthy, and they have many children. All is well that ends well. But sometimes, as I think of my esthetic operation, I find myself asking: "Did I do right? Hadn't I played a trick on Maria's fond young man?"

The surgeon gets the most satisfaction out of urgent cases, for then he assumes the rôle and importance of a miracle man. This kind of surgery is not learned out of books or in the libraries, nor is it learned in the laboratories or the dissecting rooms. No, it is learned in the daily round, from patients, or better still, at the great hospitals.

The relief station of the Central Hospital at Milan is the finest and largest school of emergency surgery in the world. Here are gathered, from the town and countryside, all the sick who need immediate treatment, and here the young doctor finds himself at grips with the strangest, most serious, and trickiest cases. He must get used to making prompt decisions, to using the most difficult expedients, and to performing the speediest operations that do not allow recourse either to books or mature reflection. Here, truly, is the surgeon's school.

When I served my apprenticeship here, I was accustomed to steel myself to a moving picture of wounds, poisonings, strangulated hernias, intestinal occlusions, peritonitis: all these tragedies, with their terrible complications. But in this surgical inferno the doctor reaches his full stature, and sometimes feels himself more powerful than death.

Imagine a child who reaches the hospital strangled by a foreign substance in his windpipe; he is stifling in the presence of his horrified and despairing parents. The calm and impassive surgeon performs a tracheotomy, extracts the substance, and saves the child. Isn't this truly a miracle?

A wounded man arrives bleeding from a severed main artery. The flow is copious, frightening. The surgeon quickly discovers and binds up the artery. The flow is arrested, and the patient is saved.

They often bring in a person wounded in the heart—a serious matter, that. Yet, if the surgeon is quick, if he can keep calm and avoid all delay, he makes an opening in the thoracic cage, finds that the heart is still beating in the pericardial sac which is much distended by blood, locates the wound, and closes it with a suture. The dying man comes back to life: he is saved.

If rogues are involved (and you see plenty at the relief station), one is apt to see strange, miraculous cures—organic resistance that is paradoxical and improbable.

One night I myself received a member of the criminal classes. After a plentiful meal in a stinking tavern in the Via Arena he had come to blows with his pals. During this foul quarrel, the knife played an important rôle, and the man was stabbed squarely in the epigastric region. He picked himself up, and refusing all offers of assistance, and rejecting any idea of going to a physician or to a hospital, he walked to his mistress' lodging, and there, bandaged up as well as possible, lay concealed three days. Then came suffering, sharp pains, frequent retching, and at last, on the fourth day, he consented to have the doctor called in. They could arrest him, send him to hard labor—if only he would not have to die.

When I examined him, he was cadaverous: the pulse was feeble, the face Hippocratic, and the stomach swollen. Immediately performing a laparotomy, I discovered a large wound on the anterior wall of the stomach, and I saw the peritoneal sac filled with blood, pus, gastric juice, pie, beans, wine, and all sorts of garbage. I hastily washed out the peritoneum, and closed the gastric wound, fully persuaded that the patient would not survive.

Not only did he live, but he went to prison, did his stretch, came out, and continued his misdeeds. A good man probably would have died.

All these cases succeeded one another in a phantasmagorical way in the eyes of the relief-station surgeon who never even has the satisfaction of making himself known to those who owe him life. The most unexpected cures, the most miraculous operations are performed without the patient (usually under ether) knowing the operator's name. When he is out of danger, he goes to other rooms, to other buildings, to the hands of other doctors.

The surgeon remains in the shade: he will never know the gratitude of the one he saved. But meanwhile he is learning; he is tempered, and ready for any emergency. His energy, employed to its fullest capacity at the relief station, will serve him when he has to operate on private patients of his own. Then he can look for gratitude, rewards, and honors, and he will find that there are always emergency cases to test the young operator's merit.

I recall one of those cases which was long discussed in Milanese society.

It was Saint Theresa's day, and I was celebrating it at my sister-in-law's. I was still at table when I was called to the phone. The request was very urgent, and I had to rush out. My patient proved to be the young son of one of the best and most distinguished professors in town. He was stretched out on a little mattress in the study of a Latin teacher to whose house he had gone, as was his custom, right after luncheon. The teacher was speaking when the boy was seized with violent pains in the stomach, and they

had increased to such an extent that he could think of
nothing better, in his terror and confusion, than laying the
child on the mattress, and calling his parents. They saw,
on their arrival, that the boy could not be taken home. A
reputable physician diagnosed abdominal colic, and asked
that a surgeon be called in.

The young man's peaked face was screwed up in a spasm
of pain; his face was pale; his stomach was swollen, and
painful to the touch. I saw at once that I had a serious case
at hand, and the parents read the conclusion in my eyes.
They were mad with anguish. The father, trembling all
over, seized my arm, and begged me to save his son. Some
months before he had lost his only daughter. . . .

I had the sick boy moved by a Red Cross ambulance to
the nearest private hospital, and I operated at once. The
peritoneum was full of liquid and remains of food, whence
I deduced the presence of a perforation caused by a
duodenal ulcer which, nevertheless, I did not stop to ex-
plore. In view of the gravity of the case, I took a few
stitches, and rapidly concluded the operation. . . .

A year later, when I was climbing one of the Dolomites,
I met a young man of healthy and robust appearance,
judging from the bronze tinge of his bold countenance:
he literally radiated the joy of living. I embraced him as
though he were my own son—this young fellow so miracu-
lously preserved a year before. Not a trace of the perforation remained.

I have said that emergency surgery gives the maximum
satisfaction . . . but it also demands the greatest sacrifices.
When the surgeon is called, he must forget fatigue, jump
from his bed at any hour, even in the heart of winter, and

defy the cold and every variety of inclement weather. I even had to leave the bedside of my dying mother.

My poor dear mamma had been in agony for some days: she had been stricken by congestion of the brain, and was dying. Little by little she had lost the use of her tongue, and sometimes she lost consciousness. . . . My brothers and I kept assiduous watch at her bedside. She squeezed our hands in blessing, and I looked sadly at the beloved face I would soon see no more. It was one of those ineffable moments when anguish, awe, and a thousand other emotions are blended with life's sweetest memories. . . . Suddenly a bell ringing broke in on my revery. A messenger from the police station at Brescia brought me word from Dr. Duse, director of the hospital at Salò, who entreated me to leave at once for Gardone Riviera, where Rizzo, the communal commissioner of police, was in a grave state. Gabriele d'Annunzio joined his entreaties to Dr. Duse's.

I reluctantly left my mother. . . . Would she be alive when I returned? However, duty called, and I left by the first train. At Desenzano I found the commissioner's car waiting. Traveling was slow: it was the terrible winter of 1929. The temperature stood at seventeen degrees below zero, and the roads were covered with ice and snow. Finally, somehow, we reached the Grand Hotel.

Commissioner Rizzo was in bad shape. His face showed intense suffering; he had a high fever and a very rapid pulse; his abdomen was tight, painful to the touch—the symptoms of an extensive inflammation of the peritoneum: in short, acute peritonitis, more or less widespread, doubtless of an appendicular origin. I had to operate at once, and I could only hope that I was not too late. Fortunately the Salò hospital was only a few steps away, and thence they carried the patient with as few jolts as possible. Within a half-hour Commissioner Rizzo was on the operating table.

Dr. Duse and I got to work at once. . . . We opened an enormous peritoneal sac filled with pus so fetid as to poison the entire organism. The peritoneal lesions were very serious, and so was the patient's condition, though the operation was performed so rapidly that the patient never realized it. A half-hour later the pulse was much stronger, and I felt that I had arrived in time. I turned the patient over to Dr. Duse's intelligent care, and jumped into the car to return to Milan.

Would my mother be alive? Fortunately, the answer was yes, and I was at her bedside when she breathed her last.

When Commissioner Rizzo realized that I had left my dying mother to go to his aid, he expressed his gratitude in words I shall never forget. He was ill for two months, and during this time he insisted that I visit him at least once a week. When he was cured, once and for all, he gave me proofs of his gratitude such as I have never received from any other living soul. He sang my praises to everybody, and recounted all the lucky stages in his terrible illness. And he spoke so loudly that the echo traveled to Rome, where the Duce had followed anxiously the course of his friend's malady.

The Duce was generous enough to confer successively two high honors on me, and (what I valued more) a large photograph of himself, attesting his esteem and cordial regards.

No less flattering was Gabriele d'Annunzio, who, after following anxiously his beloved friend's battle for life, had sent me a large signed photograph. I reproduce the dedication not because I am worthy of its praise, but because it is an earnest of his inexhaustible genius.

Al grande "medico di piaghe" Andrea Majocchi, all'incomparabile maestro che imprigiona nei suoi ferri la volontà del miracolo, e la luce della salvazione.
Il Vittoriale—Maggio di quarto 1929.

GABRIELE D'ANNUNZIO

The photographs of these two famous men are hung in my rooms, and there they shall stay as long as I live. My children will inherit them not through any vainglory on my part, but to remind them that their father knew how to do his duty under the most difficult and painful circumstances.

The happy results that I obtained in my profession filled me with an ever growing enthusiasm for the surgical art. I was so happy in my work that fatigue seemed slight, even pleasing. I had found my *métier*.

To crown my happiness, surgery gave me a precious and unexpected gift—my life's companion. I too could say that *"Galeotto fu il libro e chi lo scrisse,"* for I had met my loved Silvia—*dimidium vitae meae*—at the bedside of a patient, in my own field of activity—the Asilo Regina Elena. Hitherto I had been opposed to marriage: science and my profession literally took up all my time, and I could think of nothing else. Besides, I lived so contentedly with my mother and my brother that I needed no other family. Many times, to tell the truth, my mamma had suggested my choosing a wife . . . after all, I must think of the future when she would be leaving me forever. But every time she touched on this subject, I laughed loudly . . . and changed the subject.

But . . . one day I received an emergency call (it really was an emergency call), which took me to the bedside of a young woman stricken with an acute attack of appendicitis. The operation was thoroughly successful: the infection was checked at one stroke, and the scar was so small that it scarcely could be seen. The young husband was overjoyed, and the gratitude of the parents knew no bounds.

A young girl, with large, dark eyes, often sat with the parents at the convalescent's bedside. Well, you know how it is. . . . I noticed that though I was as busy as usual, and gave my patients the proper attention and no more, I willingly lingered whenever I felt these dark eyes upon me. Perhaps she looked upon me as a hero. For had I not saved her sister . . . so well, so brilliantly? Anyhow, all my arguments against my own marriage fell down like a house of cards.

One day I spoke to my mother before dinner, and told her of my intentions. This time she was the one who laughed loudly, laughed long and pitilessly, while I stood there blushing, and looking as sheepish as a small boy.

"At last, you are grown up, my son. Go ahead . . . follow your destiny," she said, and that was all.

That was twenty-three years ago, and our silver wedding is coming on. Poor Mamma will not be here to enjoy it, but Silvia has taken her place. Without her, I would be too alone in the world. For more than twenty years she has been my faithful companion, and though she seems slight and frail, she has sustained me in all my troubles, and though I am considered a learned man, she often sees farther and better than I do. She is my counselor and guide.

After almost a quarter of a century she is more precious to me than ever, and as I owe this blessing to surgery, I again give thanks to that art and science divine.

Chapter IX

THORNS

Mit gieriger Hand nach Schätzen grabt
Und froh ist, wenn er Regenwürmer findet.
                              Goethe: *Faust*

But in surgery all is not roses. . . . The thorns are sharp and plentiful, as even the most enthusiastic young fellow (such as I was in my youth) will soon find out.

The surgeon's life is tragic, because it develops amid misfortunes and grief and lamentations. The best-known surgeon has the worst troubles: worried faces, pleas, prayers. Weeping mothers try to read the truth on his lips even as they utter a lie . . . a lie actuated by compassion. How many times I have been forced to lie with my voice, with my eyes, without convincing!

"They are used to it," I have heard some say. Or, "Surgeons are hard-hearted." Nothing is more untrue. "I am used to everything," Mangiagalli used to say, "except one thing, and that is seeing my patients die." And the older I get, the more sensitive I become to human suffering. Is this weakness? I cannot say, but I do know that death impresses me more than formerly when, collecting all my forces, I was able to check my soft-heartedness by a stern sense of professional calm. Suffering did not depress, whereas today I sometimes cannot help but cry with my patients, some of whom I have known for only a day.

133

This life in the midst of anxiety, worry, and grief creates, in the long run, an atmosphere in which the surgeon can scarcely breathe—it is almost stifling. If all tragedies could only end well, all illnesses be cured! But the idea is absurd. Can every game be won, every arrow hit the mark?

We know too well, quite often, that the chances of saving a patient are slim: yet we must act. Sometimes the sick person is beyond help, and the surgeon reluctantly has to admit his powerlessness, and to refuse to operate.

Take, for example, that hideous disease—cancer. No one knows exactly the nature of the beast. Institute after institute is founded, societies spring up constantly, animals are sacrificed by the thousands, armies of scientists have spent their lives and fortunes, and thousands of journals and bulletins have been published. Rivers of ink have been dissipated in explaining a spate of ideas, hypotheses, theories. The result: exactly nothing. The further one goes, the more perplexing becomes the problem.

Some years ago my good friend, Senator Belfanti, had the fine idea of gathering together at his institute the most able and experienced scientists whose specialty was cancer. He invited them to lecture on its nature and origin. All the Milanese medical world went to hear the Word. . . . Unfortunately, however, not two of these great specialists were agreed, and as it even seemed that the speakers wished only to contradict those who had preceded them, the listeners left with their ideas vaguer and more confused than ever. If men of science are disagreed as to the nature and cause of cancer, how can a cure be found?

The hideous plague continues to spread and grow, seizing on an organ and establishing itself therein—without fever or pain, without making itself known. For cancer is like a thief in the night: *sicuti fur noctu,* insidious and faithless. It creeps in among the tissues, and infects the lymphatic canals and the glands.

When the victim feels the disease itself, he rushes to the surgeon, for the surgical knife has been, and still is, the best remedy. But surgery can offer a hope of salvation only if the tumor is localized at the very start. Here is the difficulty. If the diseased organ is on the surface (the skin, for example, or the breast), cure is still probable, but if an inner organ is affected (the stomach, for example), the chances of cure are negligible.

And so? . . . Well, the surgeon must perform miracles.

Miracles of technique: he must prepare himself for the most ravaging operations, for the most serious troubles while operating, from all of which he must emerge victorious, unless he wishes to hear the ironical comment: the operation was successful, but the patient died. Miracles of courage: to brave the dangers of hemorrhage, shock, collapse. Miracles of firmness and perseverance, for sometimes the undertaking thwarts his most careful precautions. After what seems to be a thoroughly satisfactory intervention, after a truly brilliant technical victory, there may come, sooner or later, a relapse: the germs multiply around the scar or in the adjacent tissues. One feels helpless. . . .

The scientist who discovers the basic cure for cancer will be humanity's benefactor—greater than the discoverer of the telegraph, telephone, or radio. But meanwhile cancer claims more victims than war, plague, tuberculosis, or syphilis, and to it the surgeon can oppose only his knife, his strength, and his will. He too suffers and battles.

Circumstances exist when the surgeon cannot refuse to

operate: he has no choice. A strangulated hernia permits no more delay than an intestinal occlusion. Not to operate means death. No matter what the patient's age or the general condition of his health, independently of any other reasons for hesitating, an operation offers the only hope of safety.

If the patient dies during the operation, there is no cause for remorse, for otherwise he had not a chance to survive. So any expedient is justified. But certain cases solicit the aid of surgery for a disease which weakens the patient, and causes him untold agony—without endangering his life. Such a disease can be cured or alleviated by dint of time and patience.

. Imagine an individual afflicted by a free hernia. An operation will cure him; otherwise he will have to resign himself to wearing a truss and to a life of rest, sacrifice, and precautions. The same is true of a woman with a uterine tumor. She can be patient, take the waters, or try radiotherapy, and so on. . . .

In such cases the surgeon assumes a great responsibility. True, an operation is indicated, but often the patient asks, "Will the operation be a success?" Now, how can the surgeon honestly answer that question?

Can he guarantee the success of an operation? Absolutely speaking, no. Relatively speaking, yes, if the surgeon, besides his own efforts, can depend on the patient's physical resistance.

There still exists a grave problem: the unknown quantity.

A clinical examination can give an approximate idea of the patient's resistance—an idea that will be nearer the exact truth in proportion to the examiner's practical experience. This clinical idea, furthermore, can be controlled through a series of laboratory tests on urine, gastric juice, blood. Nothing must be overlooked. Sometimes, however, there are bitter surprises.

The problem of the patient's resistance—weighing all the elements that can diminish the operating risk—absorbs all scientists, and is discussed at all surgical congresses, notably at the Parma meeting of 1927. The two speakers said that, after long study and examination of every element that could throw light on the subject, a surprise was possible, in spite of every precaution.

An operating risk always exists. It is not honest to guarantee any operation.

I recall an incident that happened at the beginning of my career, and which made me more cautious than ever.

I had to operate on one of my best friends and colleagues for a trifling matter: an ingrowing nail. A very brief but painful affair. So my colleague wanted an anesthetic. In view of my responsibility, as well as of my devotion to him, I took the same preparations I would have for a very serious operation. All the examinations were made, even those of the circulatory apparatus, heart, and vessels. Nothing abnormal. I chose a very experienced man to administer the very rapid anesthetic—ether, according to the patient's wishes. But the brief sleep was troubled. I felt that something was wrong, but the surgical intervention went so smoothly that the narcotic was soon interrupted, and the patient arose without any ill effects.

My colleague recovered rapidly. About a fortnight later, however, as he left his house to make his calls, he fell dead. No one knew precisely what had happened to him, as no autopsy was performed, but when I heard the news, I realized that the fatal accident could have happened a fort-

night before, during the operation. I realized what a frightful risk I had run. People would have said either that the
operation caused or, at least, precipitated the end.

Few people can comprehend the grief of the surgeon
who loses his patient, if he has reason to believe that an
operation was not absolutely necessary: in other words, if
the patient was not suffering from a mortal disease. Imagine
his anguish if he thinks that the patient might have lived
for a long time without an operation.

How anxiously the surgeon watches the patient after
the operation! The first three days are the worst—days of
sleeplessness, worry, uncertainty, and of fears that the
surgeon can scarcely hide from the patient. At last, after
the third day, one can hope. But one battle succeeds another, and a surgeon's life is an unending round of sleeplessness, worry, uncertainty, and fear.

If our patients knew what an operation costs us, they
would not envy us our career or our earnings.

"*L'âme du chirurgien,*" says J. L. Faure, "*est une âme
inconnue, et les émotions profondes, qui la remplissent et
l'agitent ne peuvent être analisées, que par quelqu'un qui
les a ressenties. . . .*

"*C'est donc une vie passionnante et troublée, que la
nôtre, et pendant laquelle nous ne connaissons peut-être pas
un instant de absolue quiétude morale.*

"*Elle a des heures de triomphe et d'ivresse, et des heures
d'amertume et de désolation. . . .*"

Anesthesia is unquestionably one of the greatest discoveries ever made: it alone constitutes a milestone in modern
surgery. *Divinum opus est humanum sedare dolorem:* it
is marvelous to stop pain during an operation. But every-

thing has its dark side, and anesthesia itself has its disadvantages. I do not mean local anesthesia, which is not always enough, or the various kind of regional anesthesia, or spinal anesthesia, which always has its shortcomings. I mean general anesthesia, which induces complete sleep.

If it is unquestionably advantageous to suspend pain and consciousness during an operation, it is just as true that the means employed offer violence to the nervous system. The proof is that we are still searching for a thoroughly inoffensive means of anesthetizing, despite all our efforts to find one. Anesthesia is always under discussion, and I still recall what was said at Genoa in 1929.

For instance: "Since an ideal, harmless anesthetic has not yet been found, and since, indeed, anesthesia is dangerous, in that it often produces lesions that are more dangerous than the operation itself, we must encourage all efforts that surgeons make to further improvements in this field."

Also: "An ideal anesthesia does not yet exist: every method has its defects, its present or future complications, contributing, along with operative shock and various other circumstances, to so-called postoperative complications."*

There are more complications than we think, some passing and trifling, others (fortunately very rare) tragic. I have never had a narcotic accident, but I recall being present at a drama of this kind, and the scene is still indelibly graven on my memory. I was attending the operative lectures given by a noted teacher, with many living examples, a score of assistants, and a finely theatrical background. The operating theater was always full, for people thronged to it, even from other faculties, in quest of sensation. That day the benches were as crowded as ever. The

* Sanvenero, *Congresso di chirurgia:* Genoa, October 23, 1929.

surgeon's subject was a young girl whose neck was deformed by a goiter.

The girl had come from the country solely to have this disfigurement removed before her marriage. They told her that only a fine surgeon could help her, for the operation is long and difficult, dangerous also. Difficult, that is, for all except this very clever professor—a veritable magician in such operations.

In a few minutes—four to eight, let us say—the most stubborn goiters were removed, as if by magic. We were quite blasé about such miracles.

That fatal morning the professor finished his lecture amid the plaudits of the crowd. He had explained the case, indicated the method of treatment. The preparations were finished, the anesthetic began to work—they were using chloroform—and the man administering it was most competent. The operation began brilliantly, the tumor was isolated and removed, the hemorrhage controlled; there remained only to ligate the vessels, and the operation was finished. All eyes were focused on that magic finger when, from the last row of the gallery to the little group of assistants, a shudder ran through the hall.

The patient was no longer breathing.

The operation was suspended immediately, the mask raised, the straps loosed, and artificial respiration applied. But the patient's face was suffused with a waxlike pallor. Nor did the assistants look so happy. . . . But the adroit anesthetizer did not abandon his calm for a moment: he went right on with the work of respiration.

All was futile.

From time to time, the work was interrupted. They

listened anxiously. The respiration had not succeeded: the pulse had stopped beating.

I looked at the teacher: he was the image of despair. The faces of the spectators were stamped with terror, anguish, disappointment. The white mantle of death had descended over the instruments of science. Slowly the operating theater emptied of spectators.

The young girl lay there, lifeless . . .

I rushed out. In the corridor the relatives were waiting, anxiously, fearfully. . . .

But if accidents due to anesthesia (fortunately very rare) terrorize the surgeon, there is another no less frightening bugbear: embolism.

Postoperatory embolism does not strike the patient during, or immediately after, the operation. The operation can proceed marvelously, the patient can awake and find himself well, and the surgeon can administer the classic purgative after five days. He can even remove the stitches on the sixth or seventh day. All is going well, so well, indeed, that on the ninth or tenth day the patient is allowed to get out of bed for the first time. But as soon as he sits up, he pales and falls back on the pillow . . . dead.

Friends and relatives have come to congratulate him, bringing gifts and flowers; they are ready for a gay time, not for the frightful tragedy they witness. Naturally, they first think that the sick man has merely fainted—a natural result of weakness combined with the shock of the operation. They call the doctor, chafe the patient's hands, apply warm compresses, inject stimulants: all in vain. What seemed incredible is true: the convalescent no longer breathes.

Horrors of this sort are rare, but they can happen at the most unexpected times.

The wife of one of my old colleagues had been suffering for some time from a uterine fibroma: a large tumor which, having its origin many years before—possibly at the time of her marriage—was probably the cause of her sterility. The good lady had much deplored her inability to bear children, but the tumor itself had bothered her little. About the age of fifty, however, the thing grew so large as to distend her stomach in an alarming fashion.

The husband, an intimate friend and colleague of a famous gynecologist, had brought him to examine his wife. The diagnosis was not especially alarming: a large uterine tumor, but as benign as possible, and just as easily extricable; a mobile tumor peculiarly susceptible to isolation; in short, the nicest tumor in the world. With things so propitious, there was no need to hesitate. Docilely following her husband's advice, the woman entered the gynecological clinic, and heavens knows that she got the best of care. The preparations were exquisitely painstaking, and the operation itself was absurdly simple.

The patient suffered no disturbance; she was as calm as a statue during the operation. On the seventh day the stitches were removed, and on the twelfth, to the accompaniment of all possible precautions, she began to get up. Settled in a comfortable armchair, she received her friends, with their gifts of candy and flowers, and blessed the moment she had decided to be rid of her inconvenience. The husband, for his part, was beside himself with joy. On the twenty-first day he had a fine and commodious carriage at the door of the private hospital. Delighted with the prospect of returning home cured, the woman dressed;

she thanked the nurses and assistants. She seemed perfectly well and happy. But as she started to go downstairs, she paled and grasped her husband's arm. They carried her into a room, and laid her on a sofa.

She was dead. . . . Not a cry, not a sigh, not a word of farewell.

When, many years later, my colleague told me the story, he was still mad with grief. He wrung his hands, and kept reproaching himself: "Why had I advised an operation?"

What, then, is an embolus, and where does it come from? A natural question. . . .

When one operates, particularly on the abdomen, certain circumstances slow down the circulation, and cause the blood to coagulate in some large veins (spontaneous thrombosis). If blood coagulates in a vein, the circulation is stopped, for the clot acts just like a stopper in a bottle. But if the clot is loosened suddenly, it follows the current of blood, and reaches the heart. This clot, which mingles with, and circulates with, the blood, is called an embolus, and embolism is the name of the disease through which it is formed. If the embolus is sufficiently large, it gravely impairs the action of the heart: the heart can no longer function, and stops. This is paralysis of the heart, followed by syncope and immediate death.

Fortunately, embolism is very rare. At the surgical congress at Warsaw in 1929, the most noted scientists alive concluded from their experience that operatory risk due to embolism ranges from .010 to .050 per cent. If, however, a young surgeon happens to draw one of these exceptional cases at the beginning of his career, he is out of luck.

The patient dies, but I can assure you that the poor surgeon is not to blame.

But there is another operative accident for which the surgeon risks, if not prison, at least the immediate loss of every shred of reputation he owes to his assiduous labors. I mean when he forgets a dressing or an instrument, and leaves it in the patient. It seems incredible that a reputable surgeon can have such a lapse—but it has happened several times.

The layman cannot understand a mistake of this kind, and when he reads about something of this sort in the daily paper, he usually bursts out in astonished laughter. The funny papers sometimes feature a surgeon who leaves various large objects in the wound, such as a hat, gloves, even spectacles.

Instruments and dressings are most often forgotten in abdominal surgery. The abdomen is a cavity normally filled with various and intricately winding viscera: it is a veritable labyrinth. In an abdominal operation, one almost always removes the organs, and replaces them in the cavity at the end of the operation. On the other hand, many instruments are used, some very minute and fine, and the organs themselves must be protected from the air by linen bands or compresses which are wound about and cover them.

It has happened, and it can happen, that a linen band or a wisp of gauze, possibly even an instrument, can be hidden among the windings of the intestines, and remain there accidentally, after the closure of the abdominal cavity.

But why do not the surgeon and his aides pay attention to the number of these objects? Alas! the operator as well as his assistants are very alert about their instruments, but

every operative act is itself so grave, so entangled in difficulties, complications, and surprises that the attention of
the most careful and experienced surgeon can be so absorbed otherwise that he may forget.

Suppose that a sudden and violent hemorrhage occurs in
the midst of a laparotomy. In one second the entire field
of operations is inundated with blood, hiding organs and
instruments. If the surgeon is not swift and calm, he may
lose his patient. During these few short moments he must
keep his presence of mind, and make his assistants keep
theirs. However, since his attention is necessarily focused
on the patient whose life he is trying to save, it can happen that during the same time all the intellectual faculties
of his assistants may be concentrated on this same all-absorbing aspect. At such a time one scarcely thinks of counting forceps and compresses; they will think of that later,
and it can still happen, in rare cases, that they can be mistaken. . . . So a bit of dressing or an instrument is left
in the wound.

If one of these rare accidents comes to the public ear, the
surgeon is irretrievably ruined. The law is relentless in such
a case: the judges will hear neither excuses nor extenuating
circumstances. The guilty man is condemned, and the
savior of humanity is cursed as a common assassin, a cynical
and careless butcher.

Fortunately, I have not been so disgraced in my long
career, though I remember well two such cases that happened in Italy.

The first happened to one of the best professors of
Italian surgery, the clinician and surgeon of a great university; the second to a surgeon of equal merit and unquestionably scrupulous and attentive, for many years the

director of the surgical wing of a hospital. I followed both cases with interest, thoroughly convinced that any others would, in their place, have been victims of the same circumstances.

The noted surgeon, operating in his clinic on a patient for a grave disorder, possibly deadly in its consequences, left a wisp of gauze in the abdominal cavity. An abscess formed, and the patient died. The case came up in the criminal court, for such negligence was judged criminal. They discussed at great length the relation of the wisp of gauze to the patient's death; they discussed whether the professor or his assistants were the more forgetful: an important matter, from the penal angle. The inquiry lasted two years, and the surgeon was finally cleared. The gauze, they said, had been put in the abdomen as a drain—intentionally, and was to have been removed later.

So the eminent surgeon was acquitted, but without his great renown, as well as the influence he brought to bear, the verdict might have been different.

The second case, though it happened many years ago, is still discussed. It was tried in various courts, and formal sentence followed the first equivocal decision. The case may have been appealed further, but of that I know nothing.

The incident was most unfortunate. A man came to a hospital to be operated on for a very serious stomach ulcer which, without an operation, would have caused his death. The long, complicated, and difficult operation even called for the use of new instruments, and gave rise to unusual and dangerous complications. The patient was cured, and after a time left the hospital.

However, after the disappearance of the first disturbances, other ones arose, for which the patient was examined and admitted to another hospital (he had gone to live in another part of the country). The X-ray showed very plainly a hemostatic forceps left in the abdominal cavity. Such a discovery gets about, and the news was soon all over the hospital. The man was consigned to a surgeon, and operated on, but the forceps was so deeply imbedded among the intestines that extrication was difficult and painful. The patient died, and the matter came to the attention of the public prosecutor.

From that moment the unhappy surgeon's life was not worth living, and I know that since then his life has been a ceaseless torment. Furthermore, it is said that he spent his patrimony on lawyers alone, though he had received nothing for operating on a hospital patient.

Fate, bad luck, the imponderable quality—these were not taken into consideration. The famous forceps, applied to a section of an organ, had slipped down, and, hidden in the abdominal cavity between the intestines, had been forgotten. But the surgeon—they insisted—should not have forgotten. When he operates, he must be omniscient and infallible. The patient's death had to be laid to one of two causes: malpractice or negligence.

To suspect the surgeon of malpractice was, on the face of it, difficult, for the accused man had dedicated his whole life to his art. He had taught at the university, and had performed thousands of successful operations during his long career at the hospital. He had saved thousands of lives. As it could not be a question of malpractice, it must be one of negligence.

It was testified that the surgeon was noted among his colleagues for a proverbial caution, carried almost to excess. All was useless. The accident had happened, and someone had to pay.

I am not qualified to discuss the legal aspect, and if I tried to discuss it, I fear that I would not know how to keep calm. Furthermore, I might be charged with bias and friendly prejudice. But I recall that I felt discomfort as I read the news of the case—the discomfort of a man who has spent his life for the good of his neighbor, and who lives with the sword of Damocles suspended over his head—a man who lives in constant fear of a possible misfortune.

I resisted the temptation to throw all my instruments out of the window, but sometimes, when I am operating, exposing myself to all sorts of trouble, I do not dare to think of those painful events. For if the thought of them crossed my mind, good-by to courage and operative resourcefulness. I would think of nothing but counting instruments and compresses.

"Les merveilleux progrès de la chirurgie contemporaine nous ont rendus difficiles," says Faure, *"dans la plus part des maladies la guérison est la règle, la mort l'exception."* No one today is astounded when the patient recovers. On the other hand, death, now that it has become rarer, painfully surprises the public.

Thirty or forty years ago, when their patients died, surgeons took it very calmly. It was bad luck, but it wasn't their fault if nature had created infections and septicemia. Today we know the causes of death, and we generally manage to avoid them. Also, when an accident happens, we ask ourselves the painful question: is it our fault? Should we not have been more exact in our diagnosis, more exacting in the choice of methods, more careful in our operative technique?

But the public is even sterner than we are. The layman does not admit that a patient must die. The general public reasons with the same simple logic used by lawyers in drawing up their indictments of surgeons who forget instruments and compresses: either the surgeon is not competent to save the patient, and was wrong to operate, or he was able to cure him, and therefore the patient should have been cured.

Well, one cannot get around such reasoning. If the patient was not cured, it was the surgeon's fault, traceable to an error in diagnosis, an error in judging the patient's resistance, or an error in technique. Briefly, incompetence or negligence.

The reasoning is even more severe in cases where the patient is not suffering from a mortal disease—cases where the operation is almost certain to succeed. Take a free hernia, for example, chronic appendicitis, an ovarian cyst. These operations *must* succeed: there is no alternative. If bad luck intervenes, the public concludes that a mistake has been made. The surgeon is judged and condemned. This idea is so deeply rooted in the popular mind that an action for damages is not unusual, if the patient has not been cured as he should have been cured.

Not long ago I was called to give my opinion in a suit for damages, brought by a woman who had fractured a forearm—a simple enough Colles' fracture. She had called a surgeon who, after an exact diagnosis, supported besides by an X-ray examination, had set the forearm, and put it in the customary plaster cast. All proceeded normally, and after the usual time the cast was laid aside, and the woman had her arm massaged from time to time.

The fracture was cured, but though careful precautions had been used, an unsightly callus had formed. The woman was far from satisfied, and claimed that her beautiful wrist was no longer the same, that she no longer had the same agility, and that she could no longer play the piano as before. She went to a lawyer, and brought a suit for damages against the surgeon.

It scarcely seems believable, but the case—it has not yet been decided—is likely to be won by the plaintiff, who claims that after the plaster cast was put on, another X-ray should have been taken to guide the perfect setting of the arm. The surgeon had wished to avoid the second X-ray not only because he thought it superfluous, but also because he wanted to spare his patient the expense.

Needless to say, many kind and generous colleagues are often involved in such actions.

Sometimes, however, gratitude is not satisfied with a cash compensation: an action for damages. The client turns to assault. My old teacher, Professor Bottini, often told me of what had happened to an excellent French surgeon who had to operate on a young man for what seemed a simple hydrocele—idiopathic, that is. Actually, it turned out to be a tuberculous testicle. To preserve the health, possibly to save the life, of the patient, the surgeon decided to amputate the organ at once. When the patient came out of the ether, he discovered the mutilation. They explained to him the seriousness of the case, but the wretch would not listen to reason, and lapsed into a kind of savage silence. He left the hospital a few days after being cured, without saying a word to anyone. He got a revolver, waited for the surgeon as he left his clinic one morning, and shot him dead.

My old teacher told this story in order to warn us that, whenever we had to perform an injurious operation, we must secure the patient's consent. In my long career I have done even more: every time that I advise an amputation or any other destructive operation, not only do I warn the patient and his family, but I require a signed statement of consent. Yet, in spite of these prudent measures, I myself have risked assassination.

I had operated on a middle-aged man, seemingly robust, but who had been suffering from an intestinal ailment for some time. The operation had been simple and uncomplicated. At first, everything seemed to proceed normally, but on the third day, for some reason or other, a paralytic ileum (paralysis of the intestine) made its appearance. All that science and experience could suggest was done. Nothing was spared, nothing neglected, but we did not succeed in overcoming the intestinal atony. Much to my regret, the patient died six days later.

The day after this unhappy event, I was just about to sit down to lunch in a very chastened mood, when the phone rang. I rose from the table, and answered. A strange voice warned me to remain indoors, and to receive no one, for the dead man's mistress had sworn to take revenge. She had armed herself with a revolver, and was waiting to kill me. The informant—a woman—added that my enemy was a hysterical type from whom anything could be expected.

I thanked my informant, and returned to the table with such a frown on my face that my wife knew there was something seriously wrong. I told her about the phone message, and she lost no time in informing the police commissioner, whom I knew well.

The fanatic, whose revolver was confiscated at once, was cowed by the warnings of the police. She was kept under surveillance for a time, and I was told that the danger had not passed completely. I did not relax my professional duties, but I cannot deny that I carefully looked around when I went out. . . . At last I grew used to the danger, and thought no more of it.

Incidents of the profession. . . . But I do not advise my son, who is studying medicine, to be a surgeon. No. I want him to choose an easier specialty, one with fewer risks— a specialty that will allow him to sleep at night, and dine in peace in the daytime. Let him choose a specialty that does not expose him to assassination, prison, or an action for costs instead of being paid for his labors.

As for myself . . . I am incorrigible. I still love this ungrateful surgery, and I must admit that I love it as I would love a lovely and capricious creature, seductive and bold, who offers me exquisite delights and jealous torments. It is the same old story. Each has his obsessing passion. The poets have said so since the world began.

The sailor hates squalls and tempests, but he still goes to sea. The warrior loves glory more than he fears the dangers of war. . . .

I think that when I stand before the Supreme Judge, a moment after my death, in my white blouse, and with my poor hands covered with blood, he will pardon me much . . . because I have loved much, and suffered much.

Chapter X

THE MIRACLE

There are more things in heaven and earth, Horatio,
Than are dreamt of in your philosophy.
                              —Shakespeare: *Hamlet*

IT WAS THE FIRST DAYS OF AUGUST—A DREADFULLY HOT
August. Every good Milanese knows what a summer in
town can be. So he sets out, if he can, the first week of that
dreaded month, and goes to the mountains, or to sea, or
even to the Orient or Scandinavia.

That year I was very tired, and the heat was stifling.
I had already planned my itinerary: I was going to spend
my vacation at Vienna and Budapest. My valises were
packed, and the day of my departure was fixed, when I
received a phone call from my good friend Vittadini, a
bigwig in the Catholic camp and the clerical party. I could
not have guessed what he was going to ask me: he wanted
me to take his place as physician to a large group of Italian
pilgrims going to Lourdes. The departure was fixed for the
next day. At the last moment, his sister had taken ill, and
he did not wish to leave her. He wanted an experienced
doctor . . . a surgeon would do.

"But I am leaving for Vienna and Budapest."

"It doesn't matter. You will go to Vienna and Budapest
some other time. This time you will go to Lourdes. You
will travel like a prince, without spending a *centissimo*, and
you will follow a magnificent route: the Riviera, Nice,

Marseilles, Toulouse, then the Pyrenees . . . and will find many interesting things in the pilgrimage itself."

Two days later I was at Ventimiglia, at the rendezvous of the pilgrims, whence the special train for Lourdes was to start. As soon as I introduced myself to the organizing committee at the railway station, I began my duties. They put at my disposal a double first-class compartment, two communicating *coupés*, one of which was reserved for the dispensary and first-aid station. All dispositions seemed to have been carefully and generously made.

Before leaving I would have liked to meet the pilgrims, but I soon saw that that was impossible. A noisy crowd was awaiting the time for departure, and interested, not in meeting the doctor, but in getting good accommodations on the train: a noisy and excited crowd of priests and laity, surrounded by pillows, blankets, wheel chairs.

"Very well," I murmured, "I will meet my flock on the train." Besides, not all the pilgrims, many of whom were in perfect health, needed medical attention. Others, on the contrary, visibly ill, scarcely moved, or showed, in their pale and ravaged countenances, the secret of their weakness. Already, in my first cursory inspection, I noted sharp profiles and cheeks flushed with tuberculosis, invalids tainted with osteitis or spondylitis.

A paralytic was stretched out on a litter—a paralytic with weak and flabby legs; in a wheel chair was a dropsical man with an enormously swollen stomach swaddled in blankets there was a cirrhotic, possibly with a liver complaint, his face almost cadaverously peakèd, his eyes large and mournful. Huddled up on a bench, a poor man, his head bandaged and his throat swathed in a heavy black scarf, had a cancer

of the cheek: his face was already ravaged by a tumor that
was monstrous to behold, and which had to be bandaged to
keep people from shuddering with horror. His throat,
tumefied by congestion of the glands, was also covered by
a scarf because of his repulsive deformity.

A little farther away, seated on another bench, a strange
couple attracted my attention: a man and woman in modest
circumstances, young, doubtless married. He held her
arm, observing her lovingly, speaking tenderly to her,
speaking words of consolation. She looked tired, but resigned. Her eyes were very soft, as blue as the skies . . .
but lackluster. She was blind. . . . Married for a year, she
had been stricken during her pregnancy by a serious disease of the optic nerve, and had completely lost her sight.
The baby had been born beautiful and strong, but she had
not seen it, and doubtless would never see it, for all had
pronounced her disease incurable.

But her maternal soul had not lost hope. As she had expressed a desire to go to Lourdes to pray the Mother of
Jesus to let her see her children some day, her husband, a
poor railroad watchman, had scrimped and saved to collect part of the money needed for the trip, and the pilgrimage committee had furnished the rest.

I looked with emotion at that young and lovely face, at
those eyes so soft and blue, opened to infinity, yet bereft
of light. . . . Would the Madonna perform the miracle?
Perhaps. She who had looked at her own child would not
refuse such a delight to this good and trusting young
mother.

But suddenly there is a noise of wheels and iron. All be-
stir themselves at the arrival of the train. Everyone rushes

to get the best place. I seat myself in my compartment, a little ashamed at being so privileged, with all this space and these conveniences at my disposal.

We leave at precisely three o'clock. Before night, we will be in Marseilles, where we will sleep at the hotel. The train runs the length of the Côte d'Azur, as if it did not wish to linger in these haunts of worldly delight so different from the pious aim of the pilgrimage. I see Mentone, an enchanting village nestling amid palms and olive trees. The villas and the gardens, the mountains and the sea about these capitals of luxury and pleasure contrast strangely with the misery surrounding me. As we pass Monte Carlo, the pilgrims intone the litanies of the Blessed Virgin: from my compartment I can hear the sacred dirge and the prayers of the sick:

Mater amabilis
Mater admirabilis. . . .

I listen as in a dream to the humble cantilena which rises and fades in the atmosphere of the gambling casino and the palatial hotels. What a difference there is between this convoy of invalids and this bower of Armida: shrines of delight, pleasure, and corruption!

After Monaco, Nice; then Antibes and Cannes . . . and the train pursues its course as the sun sets on this warm and limpid August afternoon. The sacred songs continue to rise during the early part of night.

More and more I feel my loneliness in this empty compartment: I wish to talk with someone, and to look about me, with my eyes and ears open. In the compartment next to mine is a company of ecclesiastics: His Eminence the

Archbishop of Genoa, with his entourage. They are discussing churchly matters, things above my poor ken. So I go across the way. . . . Here, the scene changes. I hear a twittering medley of feminine and childish voices—a gayer atmosphere than that of the priests. I timidly push open the door, and introduce myself.

As the pilgrimage doctor, I am a privileged character, and find no difficulty finding a conversational opening. Here are two or three Genoese families, who wish to make the pilgrimage together, combining devotion with pleasure. I do not see a sick person among them. The most distinguished of the ladies is the wife of an eminent delegate from a Genoese college—a very influential person in the clerical party. She is accompanying her two children to Lourdes, possibly (I say to myself) because her husband wishes them to go and be edified.

In the same first-class compartment is another lady, the sister of the first; she is with her thirteen-year-old daughter. To complete this lively company is a very pleasant young woman, the sister of a Genoese lawyer, who in his rôle as a committee member is traveling with the heads and organizers of the pilgrimage.

What boons could these good people, so robust and healthy, rich and happy, ask of Our Lady of Lourdes? It is hard to say. The fair young woman was the only one who could have anything to ask from the Madonna, and that was something most young women pray for: a good husband. However, these comfortable Genoese were delightful traveling companions.

We arrived in Marseilles shortly before midnight. Here we stayed the night; the next morning was taken up with a visit to Notre-Dame de la Garde. Meanwhile, I had to learn the names of the invalids, get the data on each, and listen to their case histories. I had to treat and bandage some of my flock. Happily, most of them had borne stoically the inconveniences of traveling. I ordered them to rest that night and the next morning, and I would see that they lacked nothing.

We were to leave the next afternoon. At the specified hour all were at the station: not one was missing. I passed in review the invalids entrusted to my care: a mournful company stricken by tuberculosis, osteitis, spondylitis, arthritis, consumption, cancer, and nervous disorders. The paralytic lay on his stretcher, his limbs flabby and lifeless; the dropsical man was huddled in his wheel chair, with his enormous belly covered with shawls; farther away was a dancing boy, whom I had not seen previously, afflicted with those strange convulsive spasms known as St. Vitus' dance. A poor fellow with the palsy could not make his hands hold still a second. What nameless horrors in such a small area!

They all boarded the train with but one goal in mind: hope sped them toward the miracle, toward the light of salvation.

This time the journey was longer. We had to dine on the train, and pass the night there; in the morning we arrived at Toulouse; then came Tarbes, and in the afternoon we finally entered Lourdes. It was very tiresome for the poor invalids. I found, however, that none of them was worse. No one complained, and even the most wretched were sustained by hope and faith, by the desire to reach the end of their journey.

At Nîmes, the sun set, and night came on. From my compartment I heard them chanting the *Ave Maria* and the evening prayers; again I heard the litanies:

Mater amabilis
Mater admirabilis. . . .

Then silence. The train was shrouded in silence, and it went silently on its way. No singing, no prayers. I lay down and tried to sleep, but I could not.

Would I really see miracles? Was it possible? The year before, the most amazing cures had been sworn to. Paralytics had risen and walked, the dumb had spoken, and gaping wounds had been healed. The good priest directing the pilgrimage had warned the faithful, however, not to expect many miracles. What mattered, according to the good man, was to present oneself before the Blessed Virgin with the faith that had moved mountains—the faith that had steeled the saints to the agonies of martyrdom.

Belief was what counted. If there is a cure, so much the better: it signifies that the Great Mother of God has had pity on the suffering body. But if the body remains sick, that must be for the good of the soul, and in any case the Holy Mother gives to her suitors the sweet balm of comfort and resignation. . . .

Thus the good priest had spoken, and his words still ring in my ears, echoing in my heart: for they were spoken simply, ardently.

Such convictions admit no reply: one does not argue when faith is involved.

The next day, with dawn lighting the verdant slopes

of the Pyrenees, the whole train trembled with a mighty wave of enthusiasm. We had only left Toulouse, but already all were awake, and the invalids crowded to the windows, and scanned the horizon for the spire of the Sanctuary. The more devout chanted the *Ave maris stella*, and soon I was in the midst of a babel of tremulous voices, prayers, and cries. The scene of enthusiastic faith reached its height at Tarbes, to taper off, toward noon, when the promised land was clearly in sight, and the train thundered into the station at Lourdes.

Here the confusion was indescribable. Other convoys of pilgrims had come from the most diverse regions: a green train from Paris, a white from Bordeaux, and a blue from Belgium. The station was swarming with faithful, priests, nuns, invalids, stretchers, wheel chairs; a rich confusion of cries and lamentations mingled with the whistle of the locomotives, the roar of the wheels, and the shouts of the railroad employes.

When it was a trifle calmer, I could attend to the transportation of my invalids: the less sickly to the hotel, the more afflicted to the Asile, a kind of hospital with vast barren apartments, without the slightest sanitary accommodations: a real public dormitory with beds and stretchers in abundance.

Finally, I retired to my room in a modern hotel, furnished with every possible comfort imaginable; here I found my Genoese friends from the first-class carriage. Though brimming over with enthusiasm and curiosity, that evening even they were too tired to think of sight-seeing. After the hurly-burly of the arrival and the fatigue of a sleepless night on the train, a good night's sleep seemed the best kind of restorative. We went to bed, and dreamed of blue trains and white trains, litters and invalids, cures and miracles.

But this year, we had to wait for the miracles.

It was the middle of August—almost the end of the pilgrimage season, and Dr. Boissarie, director of the Bureau of Authentications, had certified not a single miraculous cure. I do not say there were not any. In fact, some amazing cases had been reported, but the astute doctor was neither surprised nor satisfied. Mutes had spoken, paralytics or paretics had moved—there were several such cases, but these cures did not pertain to organic diseases but to functional nervous disorders.

There was talk of a case of grave pulmonary tuberculosis, with bilateral cavities, high fever, coughing, spitting of blood, profuse perspiration, and general debility. Utterly spent when she arrived at Lourdes, the patient had rested at the Asile, and despite the gravity of her condition had insisted on entering the swimming tank. While in the water she suddenly felt much better, and the objective symptoms of her disease vanished almost completely.

Taken to the Bureau of Authentications, she radiated an incredible well-being, as Dr. Boissarie noted, the observation being supported by somatic examination by several foreign physicians. Unfortunately, the preceding medical certificates were neither complete nor corroborated by the necessary laboratory tests.

A similar case came under my observation. While I was helping Dr. Boissarie in the Bureau of Authentications, a middle-aged woman was shown in. She had come to Lourdes with ulcerated sores on the inferior articulations.

These ulcerations, thought to be of varicose origin, were treated in every possible way, but without the slightest improvement. The poor woman, obliged to give up the smallest domestic task, had been reduced to desperation, and as a last resort she had decided to go, accompanied by her relatives, on the pilgrimage.

She had bathed her limbs in the piscina, whence she had been carried, half fainting, to the Asile, but in the course of the following treatment, to her astonishment, as well as to that of the attendants, the ulcers began to heal rapidly. The people cried out at the miracle, and the patient, completely cured, walked unaided to the Bureau of Authentications, followed by her relatives.

"I am cured, I am cured!" cried the woman, showing her legs, and Dr. Boissarie, patient but skeptical, made her disrobe, and lie down on the cot to be examined. On the anterior joints, corresponding to the under side of the leg and the tibiotarsal region and the instep, there were, indeed, quite recent scars, still pink and covered with a very fragile epidermis. There were no traces of lacerations, sores, or ulcers. What had happened to the sores? Dr. Boissarie examined carefully, fingered, touched, acted like a doubting Thomas. Had the sores really existed? The woman swore that they had, and her relatives said loudly: "A few minutes before the bath, not more than three days ago, her leg was one mass of ulcers: everybody knows that. . . ."

The doctor shook his head. Now, if they only had had documents, photographs, certifications from reputable physicians. But these were missing. The doctor finally decided, to the amazement of those present, not to accept as evidence the verbal testimonials of the interested parties.

He dismissed the patient kindly . . . and the miracle is not discussed further.

One of the most impressive spectacles I saw during my brief sojourn at Lourdes was the profession of the Holy Sacrament, which took place in the cathedral square. I think I have never seen anything else like it in my life.

The procession usually takes place about four o'clock in the afternoon, if the weather permits. The day allotted to the invalids under my charge had arrived, and I was invited to work with the Bureau of Authentications.

It was a fine August afternoon: warm, but airy, as is frequently the case in this delightful Pyrenean valley. I left my hotel with the impatience of a person who is avidly curious to see and to observe, for after all I had heard and read of these religious manifestations, I was naturally very interested. I took the road that led to the Sanctuary and the Grotto, but the crowd was excessive, and the hurly-burly got worse with every step I took. Pushcart dealers were hawking their sacred wares: medallions, figures of saints, statuettes of the Blessed Virgin, pictures of the Grotto and of St. Bernard kneeling before the apparition, consecrated tapers.

I tried to push through this mass of faithful and merchants, pilgrims and invalids, and managed with great difficulty to reach the Bureau. I was just in time, for the entrance would soon be blocked by the enormous crowd. I reached the place reserved for the medical corps, and took my place at the window. The crowd was surging over the vast square and up the impressive flight of stairs leading to the cathedral.

In front there stretched, hedgelike, another crowd of

afflicted, stretched out on litters, seated in wheel chairs, held up by cushions. From the faithful arose a confused medley of prayers, groans, and delirious invocations: sacred hymns alternated with cries and lamentations. Some were calling loudly on the Blessed Virgin, and others were twisting or stretching their hands toward the Sanctuary in ecstasies of bliss. The poor invalids were trembling in their wheel chairs, with the oddest expressions on their faces.

But one cry dominated all others:

O Seigneur, guérissez nos malades!
Figlio di Davide, abbi pietà di noi. . . .

A mighty cry, almost savage, persistent, obstinate. . . .

Beholding that vast and delirious crowd, that scene of suffering humanity and high exaltation, I asked myself what would happen at the procession of the Holy Sacrament. Fortunately, I perceived a whole corps of stretcher-bearers, fine, robust young men, stationed around the square—voluntary aides, splendid athletes, furnished with ropes to hold back the crowd and protect the procession.

My charges were almost all there: I saw the poor blind woman and her husband, the paralytic on his stretcher, and the dropsical man in his wheel chair, his swollen stomach covered with shawls. But their faces were unrecognizable, almost transfigured, and their eyes were shining with faith and hope. . . . A strange excitement possessed them. Even the boy with St. Vitus' dance was twisting his wretched body more than ever, and the paralytic was trembling violently.

But soon the glances of all were focused on the cathedral. A savage cry rose from thousands of throats, and the procession began its slow and solemn descent from the church. First came the clergy with the cross, followed by the delegates from the various pilgrimages, with their gold-embroidered banners; then the priests chanting the praises of God, and finally the glittering golden baldachin, borne by four ecclesiastics. Under it, in a glory of gold and precious stones, was the Holy Sacrament, carried reverently by a prelate of high degree.

The procession descends slowly toward the right side of the vast square; the crowd sways and surges like a tempestuous sea. The prayers become shrieks, the faces assume strange, unearthly expressions. The arms, the hands of the afflicted stretch toward the baldachin, when suddenly a piercing cry rings out in the prelate's vicinity: a sick woman rises from a wheel chair, throws off her covers, and stands up. The crowd goes mad. The woman is assailed on all sides, and in the tumult she risks being crushed, stifled. All want to see the woman who has been singled out, all want to touch her. Those nearest embrace her in an excess of enthusiasm.

The stretcher-bearers shield her with great difficulty, forming a protective shield around her. And thus she is escorted to the Bureau of Authentications. The door opens to admit her. The crowd of the curious, who try to invade the Bureau, are repulsed with some difficulty.

The young woman is still beside herself with excitement, almost delirious. She seems entranced, wild-eyed, and she repeats the same words over and over again, almost mechanically: "I am cured, I am cured. . . ."

Dr. Boissarie, accustomed to these scenes, does not lose his composure. He lays her gently on the cot, and lets her rest a few moments, while he tries to gather from the relatives some idea of the past history of the disease. But they too seem bereft of their senses: they can only babble incoherently. Her sister, however, hands him a certificate from a doctor in Paris, which testifies that for ten years the young woman has suffered from dorsolumbar spinal tuberculosis: spondylitis which developed slowly, and which was treated in every known way—special corsets, sun cures, iodine cures, etc.

The sick woman developed a hump, and finally the lower limbs were paralyzed to such an extent that she had to keep to her bed. In the past few years she was not able to stand on her feet, much less walk. To these particulars was added a summary of the hump and of a large cold abscess which occupied, when she left Paris, the right iliac fossa. This abscess should have been tapped, on the physician's advice, but the patient, before undergoing further treatment, had wished to go to Lourdes. Quite on her own responsibility she had traveled there, borne on a litter (for she could not move), and accompanied only by her relatives.

Dr. Boissarie quickly read the report, and then began to examine the invalid, who had calmed down somewhat. She had an obvious though not painful dorsolumbar hump; of the cold abscess in the iliac fossa there remained not a trace. The mobility, sensitiveness, and reflexes of the lower limbs were perfectly normal. Though the muscles were slightly atrophied, the young woman could move and raise her legs. Asked to rise, she stood up, and walked about.

An exclamation of surprise came from those present, among whom were several physicians. Boissarie reread the report, but he seemed unconvinced. He would have to have other proofs: a more detailed clinical history, X-rays. . . . Now, if the doctor who had treated her had only come in person! . . . Furthermore, the two women, the invalid and her sister, had come to Lourdes without being attached to a pilgrimage, and so the patient lacked even a testimonial from the physician on the train.

The doctor questioned the relatives again, and examined the girl. Conscientious as he was, Boissarie seemed perplexed: he did not know what to decide, and at last he wisely concluded to keep the invalid under observation before making his decision.

The procession of the Holy Sacrament was over. The crowd had dispersed in various directions: some to the vast basilica, others to the Grotto, and others still to their *pensions* or hotels. The cosmopolitan throng was still quivering with emotion.

I abandoned my post of observation, said good-by to Dr. Boissarie, and slowly returned to my hotel, amid that babel of pushcart merchants and noisy pilgrims, without seeing anything, without paying the slightest attention to anything. My brain was too crowded with impressions, my soul too full of emotion. I still saw those ecstatic faces, those pleading, tearful glances; I still heard that heart-rending cry:

> *O Seigneur, guérissez nos malades!*
> *Figlio di Davide, abbi pietà di noi!*

I saw the arms stretched toward the shining gilded baldachin, almost as if to do violence to the divine will, as if to storm very heaven in their quest for grace.

I kept seeing the sick woman with the ulcerated joints, the young girl with spondylitis. How could these cases be explained? By what unknown metabolism had these wounds, of many years' duration, been healed in a few days? Doubtless they had existed, for the recent scars testified to them. Possibly the ulcers were not of varicose origin; possibly the diagnosis had been wrong. But even if they were of another sort—tubercular or syphilitic, for example—would they heal in a few hours? The relatives had testified to the rapidity of the cure, and better still, so had the attendants at the Asile, who had treated the ulcers some days earlier.

And the girl with spondylitis? Was her cure any less odd? She had a medical certification of recent date, and this certainly carried weight. Tuberculosis of the last dorsal and first lumbar vertebrae was evident, for the hump was still visible; paralysis, or at least, paresis, of the lower joints certainly existed, as the invalid had been bedridden for so long a time. But we must not forget the atrophy of the muscles. Investigation might reveal that, during the long illness, the inflammation had cleared up, and the lesions had healed. Further, the nervous components in the rachidian canal could have been strengthened, finding once again conditions needed for their functioning. (For the patient, bedridden so long, might have been unaware of the possibility of their functioning.)

Perfect reasoning. But the cold abscess—how about that? That large iliac abscess noted by the physician before the patient's departure for Lourdes, and which he wished to tap? Where had the pus gone? Possibly the fatigue of the trip and, more especially, the jolts of the train had ruptured the abscess, and the pus had drained into the bladder or intestine, for example, thence to be carried off in the urine or fecal matter. But since when did an iliac abscess of spondylitic origin open into the bladder or rectum? And even supposing such had been the case, would not the young girl have noted the excess of pus in her urine or feces? There was nothing absolute in my clinical reconstruction of the case, and there were certainly many odd facts whose presence together was nothing short of inexplicable.

These thoughts troubled me all evening, and even robbed me of sleep during the night. When I rose the next day I was still tired and preoccupied, and I had almost forgotten that the pilgrimage was to return to Italy that afternoon.

These few days of pilgrimage, rich with emotion and surprise, had passed quickly.

At three o'clock the Italian pilgrims were to meet at the station. All were on time. On the train I rejoined my traveling companions, who were loath to leave so quickly; they would willingly have remained in this land of dreams and enthusiasm.

I reviewed the invalids and cripples. They were in the same condition as before: no cure, no improvement. I expected complaints, recriminations, words of disillusionment. I was wrong. I found them all resigned, almost comforted. Some planned to return the following year, since the Blessed Virgin had not hearkened to their prayers. Others were firm in their faith, certain that they would be cured after their return. They had prayed to the Virgin at Lourdes, and they would continue to invoke her: grace would be their reward. Had it not been written: *Pulsate et aperietur vobis?* All the pilgrims were filled with a feeling of well-being—a force of soul, a strange and ineffable serenity, an affecting resignation.

I found my blind girl, blind as before, in a third-class

carriage. She was curled up in a corner, with her husband's arm about her. I asked her how she felt. She recognized my voice, for I was much interested in her, and previously had expressed my profound desire for her recovery. Now I could only say that I hoped she would be cured after her return. She thanked me with emotion, and said, "If God wishes, I will be cured; but I am happy just the same, for I know that I will see my children in paradise." Amazed and chastened, I brushed the tears from my eyes. . . .

All these people, who had gone to Lourdes to be cured, had made sacrifices, and had undergone agonizing pain because of the inconveniences of traveling, without obtaining the slightest alleviation of their misery. Yet they returned home resigned, comforted, serene. Not a word of discouragement, not an accent of rebellion.

Chapter XI

THE ACCIDENT

AN AUTOMOBILE IS A FINE THING.

In my youth automobiles did not exist. When doctors were in a hurry, they used a carriage or a bicycle. Now the bicycle has gone down in the world, and is used only by workmen and peasants; but formerly it was almost a luxury, and doctors found it very useful. I recall that the portico of the hospital was transformed, during visiting hours, into a parking place for bicycles. Now, however, the grand courtyard functions as a garage, where one can see as many makes of car as one does at an exposition.

Yes, the automobile is a great help to doctors, especially to surgeons, who have to rush around on emergency calls: they are constantly on the move, going from one part of the great city to another in the course of their visits and consultations. It is also a great boon to the weariest of all workers who, during a half-day in the open air, can forget the eternal maladies and sorrows of professional life. For them the automobile is a delightful tonic for fatigue; for a few hours at least, it gives the slave of duty the illusion of liberty.

But the automobile can also be a faithless and dangerous companion, particularly for those bold spirits who think they can drive while thinking of other things.

One fine Sunday in November I went with my family

for an excursion in the country. Our destination was the
smiling Brianza country and the ever enchanting banks
of the Lario, but it was my fate, that night, to bear a new
patient to my clinic, and I am sure no other patient has
ever been treated more tenderly.

We had stopped at the monastery of Mandello, resting
at a delightful tavern on the shores of the lake. Olive trees,
cypresses, the garden still in flower, white chrysanthemums,
the golden leaves of the plane trees swaying in the breeze,
the rays of the sun casting witchfire over the snowy peaks
of the Grigne and the cliffs of San Martino: all conspired
not only to make me forget the cares and anxieties of my
profession, but also the hour of return.

Night began to fall, and with the dusk a very light mist
danced across the plain. Reluctantly, we started home.
Taking the wheel, I followed the Lecco road, and soon we
had left the bridge over the Adda, Merate, Monza, and
Sesto San Giovanni behind us.

We were now on the Milan road: we felt practically
safe at home.

I put on my headlights, and slowed down. A sudden
association of ideas made me think that at a certain time
I must be at the clinic. My holiday was over. In my mind's
eye I saw the patients I had left for some hours. . . . How
was that damned peritonitis case getting on? . . . And
that gastro-enterostomy I had performed yesterday?

Suddenly an agonized cry burst from our throats. . .
A gray shadow had come from the side road on the right
and was running across the road. I put on the brakes, and
twisted the car to the left . . . but the shadow was in
the way of the right mudguard. The car stopped across

the road, and we all got out: a woman was lying in the road; she was unconscious, and gave no signs of life.

My cousin, who was with us, bent over her. She was breathing feebly, and the pulse was imperceptible. My daughter was crying, my wife was faint, and I myself was bewildered, paralyzed. It was now very dark. I picked the woman up, and laid her across the back seat. Was she still alive? . . .

Leaving my family in my cousin's care, I started the car again in order to take the woman, dead or alive, to the hospital. Since no one wished to accompany me, I was left alone with my dismal burden. But the car did not go, and after a short time I got out to see what the matter was. A broken fender was scraping against a right wheel, and there was also a slight bump on the fender. I remedied the matter, and proceeded on my way.

I tried to hurry, but my hands trembled on the wheel. I was frightened . . . from time to time I turned around, and looked at the back seat. The motions of the car had changed the woman's position, but she gave no other sign of life. . . . At the Porta Venizia I was stopped a moment by cross traffic, and had a chance to get a better look at my passenger, whose limbs had been exposed by the jolting of the car. I slapped her slightly, but she gave no sign of life.

At last I arrived at the hospital, and summoned help.

The attendants lifted the poor creature; a nun arrived on the scene, followed by a policeman. They took her in the dispensary, and laid her on the cot. At last I saw what she looked like: she was a middle-aged woman in a state of absolute unconsciousness. Her face was cyanotic, congested, and her breath came feebly, raspingly. At any rate, she was still living. . . .

The staff doctors rushed around, undressed her, examined her. The pulse was feeble, intermittent; the head was covered with bumps and contusions. The right forearm was fractured. But her general condition was what worried me the most.

I told the policeman the details of the accident, and entrusted the poor woman to my colleagues; then I thought it best to leave. . . . But during the evening Sister Agostina phoned me. The situation was getting worse, and she advised me, as did the physician and the policeman, to stay in hiding for at least twenty-four hours. If the patient died, they would have to arrest me.

My terror-stricken wife insisted that I sleep elsewhere, and sent me to my cousin's house. But how could I sleep? Scarcely had I arrived at my host's than I wanted to return home to my own family. I could not sleep. That sinister shadow crossing the road was ever before my eyes. I started at every noise, and tossed in my bed. Finally I arose and walked the floor. That damned automobile!

Well, before the dawn, I could stand it no longer. I rose, dressed, and went out into the dark and silent street; I walked swiftly through the side streets, and returned to the hospital. I entered on tiptoe, and passing through the well-known corridor, I arrived at the infirmary where the dying woman ought to be . . . if she were still alive. Thank God, she was still there, on her bed in the corner. . . .

I approached stealthily. The woman was gasping; she seemed to be sleeping. Her pulse was beating, but it was definitely a cerebral pulse . . . choppy, feeble, intermittent. As she had had no hemorrhage of the ears or nose, it was safe to assume there was no fracture at the base of the brain.

A nun saw and recognized me. She told me that after being put to bed, the woman seemed near death. Then the pulse gained strength . . . more strength. She had not yet regained consciousness, but she had murmured a few words.

"She was not killed by the blow, so perhaps she will recover."

It was day. I felt a little less worried, but I did not feel like killing time. I decided to consult an attorney. At the office of the insurance company, where I had gone to report the accident, I saw my relative in the legal department: the lawyer Acerbi, a great specialist in accidents, astute as they're made and as wise as a serpent. He tried to calm me down.

"Relax," he said. "If things were as you say, it's O.K. Of course, it isn't enough just to be right: you must be able to prove it—you must have witnesses, proofs. I'll think the matter over. Try to save the woman . . . it's your job and your duty. . . . Get it?"

I understood perfectly. His words roused me. My duty was to summon up all my surgical resources. And as I have said, I do not think any other patient has ever received more careful treatment. When I returned to the hospital, the poor creature had shown some signs of consciousness. Her right side was paralyzed, her left slightly paretic. She had, however, recognized her lover who, the night before, had arrived on the scene, breathing vengeance and demanding reparation.

The next day she was so much better that I asked, and obtained, permission to have her transferred to my building. I was not sure whether I was doing right or not. My aides disapproved. They believed that I ought not to assume the responsibility of the cure to play the dual rôle of doctor and accused. They were right, at least theoretically. Meanwhile, I mobilized my entire staff in behalf of my patient. She was lodged in a special absolutely sound-proof room and there my skilled assistants attended her. All my aides— and they were many—were at my beck and call.

I also got the neighboring neuropathological building on the job. Its noted specialists, some of them internationally famous, spared neither their talents nor themselves in giving me a helping hand.

The queen of England would not have fared better. Yet, despite all this care, the course of the malady was tempestuous. And it was a terrible ordeal for me. For more than a month I hovered between hope and despair, and if this experience did not make me neurosthenic, nothing ever will.

At first we struggled against death, then against invalidism.

With the most delicate X-ray machines we probed the deepest folds of the cranial base, in trying to find the fracture that was never found. The cephalospinal liquid containing blood, and so-called pyramidal symptoms, as well as peresis of the various segments, indicated a cerebral contusion. One day, when the pulse descended to thirty-four beats a minute, we argued about the advisability of operating: it was suspected that the compression was due to a hematic tumor.

I did not want to operate.

Much later, when her general condition was improved,

and cure was assured, I must have been mad to fear cerebral complications: traumatic psychosis. My anxiety grew. Already I saw my victim insane, unable to work, confined to an asylum. Death was better than that.

Again I lost my appetite, again I spent sleepless nights. My despairing wife was at her wits' end. In time, this particular madness disappeared. Now I began to worry about the fracture of the forearm. An X-ray showed that the bones, which at first had been set well, were really badly placed, naturally to the patient's extreme discomfiture. We had to start the apparatus three times again, carefully watching the patient to see that the invalid did not move.

But another surprise still awaited us: when the bandage was removed, we found that the radial nerve was paralyzed, probably from compression. This proved susceptible to massage and radiotherapy, and finally this last ailment was cleared up.

At last, the patient was able to leave the hospital in perfect health, as shipshape as the insurance people required. With all her suffering, she had gained weight, while I had lost twenty-five pounds. This time the real sufferer was myself!

So ended the accident.

There was no criminal action. I did not have to stand in the dock, for my colleagues at the hospital had viewed the case with the greatest optimism, saying from the very start that the case was curable within thirty days.

As I had insurance, and as indemnity was paid at once, there was not even a civil action. The accident only cost me a few lire for repairing the fender and the mudguard, which were not insured. But the shadow of this terrible evening weighed on my mind.

And I must not under any circumstances forget my fright.

The guilty car remained in the garage, and for several months I had not the courage to look at it. After the woman had left the hospital, I tried to take the wheel. . . . Every time that a pedestrian crossed the street, I trembled, and I thought of that luckless shadow, that fateful crossing, and the way my daughter cried. I thought of that lugubrious drive back, when I knew not whether I was transporting a live person or a corpse.

The story is not very brilliant, and I have told it humbly, in a minor key. I want to remind myself (if not others) that an automobile ride is sometimes the most perilous and most difficult of operations.

Chapter XII

THE SECRET

THE PROFESSIONAL SECRET IMPOSES A MORAL OBLIGATION ON the surgeon, just as it does on any doctor. Woe unto the surgeon who does not take seriously this obligation which adds something sacred to his mission. Woe unto the doctor who, through neglect, flippancy, or inattention, reveals the smallest item from this precious collection of data, confidences, and confessions entrusted to his care.

He is, or ought to be, like a priest. The inviolability of the professional secret must be interpreted in the most absolute sense of the phrase, and should even prevail over the authority of the courts when professional scruples conflict with judiciary search for truth.

When I was an obstetrician, I often found myself in critical and contradictory situations. For example, I was once called to intervene in a case of severe hemorrhage following a criminal abortion performed by certificated midwives. On the premises I found irrefutable proofs of the crime: for example, a lancet or a bougie. Other times, still more serious and tragic, I found the uterus punctured by a criminal instrument, used for inducing abortion, and had to rush the woman to the hospital for a hysterectomy—in other words, ablation of the uterus. Only in that way could she be saved.

In such cases, if the patient dies, the surgeon's duty is simple, clear, and precise. He must inform the prosecuting attorney of the criminal deed: the crime against mother-hood. Then competent authority will consider his duty done.

But if the patient does not die, the surgeon faces a dilemma: on one hand, he ought to denounce the criminal abortion just as he would any other crime; on the other hand, in doing so, he imperils his client, who is equally guilty, but whose secret he cannot betray. What can he do? It is a ticklish question, one that has not yet been solved. It rises not only in cases of criminal abortion, but in many other situations surgery deals with: wounds, quar-rels, crimes of all descriptions. . . .

In the days when I was an obstetrician, the tendency was to safeguard absolutely the professional secret: there was no denunciation, unless the patient died. Now that meas-ures against criminal abortion are more rigorous than ever, it seems to me that the tendency is to legalize repudiation, or at least some limitation, of professional secrecy.

I say *seems* advisedly, for I still do not understand thor-oughly the actual dispositions, and if I do not understand them, it possibly follows that they are not very clear . . . or that I have not fathomed them.

It is certain that the professional secret sometimes puts the surgeon to a hard test. I do not mean the small indis-cretions that the public attributes to us behind the patient's back, in drawing rooms and clubs. Sometimes even the sanctuary of our private office is invaded, and we are ques-tioned and sounded out in all possible ways. Of course, we are not allowed to speak. It is an ordeal I have undergone often, and so have a great number of my confreres.

One day I had to perform a nephrectomy on a lovely

and charming woman suffering from renal tuberculosis. The young creature was sensitive, intelligent, and attractive. Nevertheless, she had neglected her health for some time. I had uncovered an unquestionable syndrome: disturbances in the urinary tract, pains in the right side, ischuria, pollakiuria. The patient previously had had pulmonary symptoms, but these had been alleviated. I made all the necessary examinations, and concluded that the right kidney was tubercular. I suggested an operation: the kidney would have to be removed. The patient agreed, and the operation was performed. The patient recovered and seemed, at least in appearance, quite normal.

I had not seen her for a year, when a young man and an elderly woman were ushered into my office. The young man explained the visit. "I am the fiancé of Miss X, your patient, and this lady is my mother. The marriage will soon be performed, but before going ahead I wish to have some precise information about Miss X's health. You treated her. . . . Now, just what was the nature of her disease? Is my fiancée completely cured? In other words, is she eugenically fit for marriage?"

I recalled perfectly the nature of the operation, as well as the previous pulmonary lesions. I felt that the young girl was not strong. She lacked one kidney, and lesions of the same nature could appear again. To my mind, she was not fit for marriage. Had she been my daughter, I would not have given her my permission, nor would I have wanted such a wife for my son.

Furthermore, pregnancy can be very dangerous for such a person, since it predisposes her to an onslaught of tuberculosis, and awakens latent and dormant lesions. Even if this did not happen, what would happen to the children born of such a marriage? No, I could not allow a misdeed of this sort. As a physician, as a surgeon, I must oppose it. But how could I draw the young man from the abyss yawning at his feet? I was forbidden to betray a professional secret, no matter what the reason.

I did honestly all that I could. . . . I hesitated, I seemed undecided. I said that it was impossible for me to reply to such questions, that I had not seen the young woman for a year, and that I knew nothing of her present health. There is a proverb about a word to the wise. . . . But my words were not understood, or at least they were not interpreted as I had hoped.

The young man was evidently in love, and when one is in that state, good-by to reason. The marriage took place . . . unfortunately. A few months of illusory happiness, then pregnancy: the young wife's delicate health was affected. First came pleuritic, then pulmonary troubles. An abortion had to be performed, after which the patient declined in health, and died.

If I had only been able to suspend professional secrecy, even for a moment!

But sometimes, by keeping a secret, the surgeon can, in the face of certain delicate situations, avert the ruin of an entire family, and bring peace and happiness to all. How many masculine peccadillos are winked at, how many feminine ones hidden!

No one has the right to invade that sanctuary where professional secrets are jealously guarded. By sticking to this maxim the doctor performs a double service: first by his service, then by his silence. I worked on this principle many times, and so, too, did one of my colleagues in a case of

extrauterine pregnancy which merits telling, because it was
so out of the ordinary.

First, however, a word of explanation for the layman.

An extrauterine pregnancy is an awful bogey to the obstetrician: a strange nosological entity fraught with tragic
complications and diagnostic surprises, to avoid which he
must be constantly alert and unstinting in his care.

Everyone knows that the marvelous phenomenon of
procreation demands a female principal, the ovule, and a
masculine, the spermatozoon, the latter developed in the
male sexual gland, the former in the ovary. But for fecunda-
tion to take place, the two elements must meet and mingle.
Where do they meet? Customarily in the oviduct, a long
and winding canal that connects the ovary with the uterus.
Here the ovule arrives from the ovary, the male element
from the outer organs.

They meet, and what induces their attraction is the eternal law that governs procreation and the survival of the
species. They meet, and then, inextricably united, they
make their way to the uterus, where the uterine mucous
shelters and protects them. There they will be nourished
as they mature, and the uterus, generous and provident
host, will shelter the egg in its growth, through the entire
course of the pregnancy, and then will expel the finished
product of the conception: *the son of man.*

The rest is well known, for we have all followed the
same road into the world. But what is not so well known
is that the two elements, after they have met, sometimes
lose their way. Why? No one knows precisely, the thing
is so intimate and secret. At any rate, instead of reaching
the uterus, the embryo develops elsewhere: in a Fallopian
tube. Such a divagation may spell disaster for the woman.

A Fallopian tube, unlike the uterus, is not fitted to receive the product of the conception: it cannot support the ever-growing organism, for its walls are narrow and unyielding, unfit for expansion. At a certain point in the stretching process, they break. Blood vessels, arteries, and veins share this fatal, inevitable rupture, and the blood drains copiously into the abdominal cavity, that is, into the peritoneal recess. Thus ensues an internal hemorrhage, because no part of the blood can flow out. The woman becomes anemic, and unless the surgeon can offer a prompt remedy, she loses blood very rapidly, and dies.

The tragedy occurs with brutal suddenness, and the doctor who is aware of the situation must, after a careful diagnosis, get his patient to a place where an operation can be performed under optimum conditions. Woe unto the doctor who makes an error in diagnosis, woe unto him who marks time and delays!

Diagnosis is not always easy. It is almost impossible before the tragic attack, which, in manifesting itself, often takes on aspects that can fool the most experienced clinicians. Acute abdominal syndrome (which can be confused with many analogous complaints) is one aspect, and yet this very syndrome, in my opinion, is accompanied by a symptom which always guides me in my diagnosis: anemia —the extreme pallor due to the internal hemorrhage.

Now that my parenthesis is over, I will let my friend Dr. Wundarzt take up the story he told me at Rochester, while we were waiting for the operating hour at the Mayo clinic.

"One November evening," he began, "I was called by a colleague in the case of a woman in high society. Her condition was most grave. It seems that she had dined with friends at a restaurant, and had eaten, among other things, various highly seasoned foods: seafood, lobster, sardines, anchovies, tinned meat. After the banquet, she was seized with violent pains in her stomach, followed by vomiting and syncope. She had been taken home, and the doctor, who had been summoned at once, found her in the throes of an abdominal colic. She was a married woman, but her husband had been away a year, kept abroad by his big business deals. Information furnished by the relatives and supported by certain appearances, especially a somatic examination, suggested poisoning by spoiled food: in short, a case of botulism. The testimony of those present that the patient had eaten canned goods had, in conjunction with the retching, seemed convincing.

"The doctor had used emetics to induce further vomiting, and had even administered a purge. But as the patient grew worse, he had sent for a surgeon, considering that his responsibility was too grave, in view of the woman's position in society.

"I rushed over, and arrived at the height of the tragedy. There was a coming and going of servants, chambermaids, relatives, and friends, all in a state of terror and excitement. It seemed unbelievable that the young and lovely woman, who had been so gay during dinner that very evening, was lying there so dangerously ill. What had happened? What poison had she absorbed? How could it be explained, since all there had eaten the same food without any ill effects?

"I entered the bedroom where the lovely patient was lying, pale and lifeless. Whenever she gained consciousness, it was only to complain of the sharp pains in her stomach, particularly in the pit, to the right. Then she fell back in a faint. What was it? Appendicitis? A perforation? Peritonitis? I examined her, but could find no objective symptom that shed light on her seizures. But this pallor, this extreme bloodlessness, this fainting condition—all were signs of a severe hemorrhage. . . . But where was it? I thought of extrauterine pregnancy . . . but no, the husband had been away a year. But time was flying, something had to be done. I told the relatives that it was an attack of acute appendicitis—possibly the appendix had been ruptured. There was danger of peritonitis. . . . I told the relatives this because it was imperative to get the patient to the hospital at once.

"The family—mother, parents-in-law, brothers—all lost their heads . . . but they let me have my way. A half-hour later, the young woman was on the operating table, and only I and my assistants were present. I wanted no one else about: internes, nurses, midwife, not even the family doctor. I looked at my assistants, and swore them to silence. The Fallopian tube was emptied, the blood evacuated. Then I looked at the appendix. . . . I have never seen a healthier one. Nevertheless, I extracted it. The operation was done quickly, and my assistants bent all their efforts to rousing the beautiful woman who lay there like a waxen image.

"Would she pull through? I left the patient for a moment, and destroyed the Fallopian tube, the embryo, and all the proofs of pregnancy. The appendix? By no means. That I kept, and showed to the family who were waiting anxiously in the corridor. I showed it to them very triumphantly, pointing out the lesions (which did not exist) and the perforation (which I had made artificially) . . . the perforation that would have caused peritonitis and, almost certainly, death.

"But would the poor wretch really pull through? I read this anguished question in the eyes of the parents and relatives, among whom was not the husband . . . and a good thing he wasn't!

"The postoperative treatment was not easy. The patient was exhausted, and despite all our precautions, on the point of death. The third day, she was slightly better, but now there were symptoms of peritoneal inflammation. This time I really thought she was going to die. She was, however, completely conscious. She asked for a priest, and remained alone with him longer than her strength permitted. What had she told him? No one, of course, will ever know, since the confessor, like the surgeon, must maintain his professional secrecy. Well, what could she have confessed? A fatal error, a moment of abandon, a few hours of oblivion. . . .

"After her confession, however, the patient improved. Her pulse became stronger, and, at the same time, she gained strength. The symptoms of peritonitis faded away. A month later she left the hospital, her health regained. And before leaving she wanted to tell me how grateful she was. She called me into her room, and when we were alone, burst out crying.

"This was more than I could bear . . . I dashed out. Of course, I realized all that she had not dared to tell me. Yes, she was grateful. I had saved her life, and with it something, to her husband and children, more precious still: honor and peace."

Chapter XIII

DUELING

I HAVE NEVER APPROVED OF OR UNDERSTOOD DUELING, AND I have always hesitated to lend my talents in such cases. Thrice, however, I could not refuse. Once I received an order that admitted no argument, and twice I had to act for friends, relatives even. If I had refused to help, the duel would have taken place anyway, and the surgical dispositions might have been entrusted to less experienced hands. If anything serious had happened, I would never have forgiven myself.

But the duels I witnessed were such tame affairs that they gave me an even lower idea, if possible, of that stupid hangover from the Middle Ages.

The first time I hearkened to the insistent prayers of a very dear colleague.

The matter (in which a lady was involved) concerned one of his relatives, an artillery officer who had been insulted at the theater by a celebrated Milanese lawyer. A challenge had followed, and when I read the procedure of the meeting, I shuddered to my marrow. The duel was to be with sabers, with no strokes barred, and the fray was to continue until one or the other was unable to stand up. However, the physicians were empowered to stop the duel when one of the two was all in.

"Good Lord," I ejaculated. "What barbarism! We poor

188

doctors spend all our time preserving our neighbors' health, and keeping sickly and delicate people alive, and here are two fine men, useful to society and in perfect health, who wish to lose their physical wholeness at any price, and for that matter, their lives, too, if God so wills. And possibly the one who pays will be the one who is right. . . ."

I had never before witnessed a duel, but I thought of all the serious wounds I had read about in the papers. I recalled the fate of poor Cavallotti: the point of the saber pierced his mouth, and cut the carotid at the maxillopharyngeal triangle. The celebrated man died in a few moments of hemorrhage and asphyxia, for the hematic fluid, in torrential volume, clogged the respiratory tract before the attending surgeon (he was a very great surgeon indeed) had time to intervene.

The poor doctor was severely criticized, but how could he ligate the vessels in such surroundings—the terrace of a villa—and without aid and materials? Such an operation is no simple matter even in an operating room, with plenty of assistants and all the necessary materials.

Other severe accidents came to my mind: strange lesions I had read about in treatises, novels, and tales. . . . I racked my brain to think of some means of averting disastrous outcome. I cursed the barbarous and stupid institution, and I was even tempted to withdraw. My responsibility, in the event of an accident, seemed excessive, not to mention the annoyance of being surprised by the authorities, and spending some time in a cell.

But I had accepted the nasty commission, and I could not go back on my word. I eased my conscience by making the most elaborate preparations. I ordered my aides at the clinic to be ready for an emergency, for if my client were seriously wounded I would have to get him to the right place at once. I also asked my many assistants to let me know where they could be reached at a given hour, and to hold themselves ready for any emergency. I prepared my case of sterilized instruments, a little chest of drugs, bandages, ligatures, tourniquets, rubber gloves, blouses, etc.—in short, a veritable arsenal that could be placed in a car, and carried to the field of battle.

I could not sleep the night before the meeting, and I was out of the house at sunrise. I went to my nursing home to collect the instruments, and to see that everything was sterilized and in order. At eight o'clock one of the witnesses called for me. I deposited my arsenal in the car, and we departed.

The duel was to take place at the San Siro race track. Between the stables and the grandstand was a grassy plot of ground, where the horses were exercised. Sheltered from indiscreet glances, the matter had to be decided there. When I arrived, all the others were ready, except the opponent's doctor. I was presented to my client: a fine-looking man of military bearing, congenial and frank in manner.

"What a shame!" I exclaimed to myself. "It's absurd to risk life and limb. At any rate, I hope he won't be the victim." He had every physical qualification one could wish: he was strong, slender, agile, and muscular—it was truly a pleasure to look at him. His opponent, on the other hand, was fat and oily: an easy target.

What a wretched place for first aid! A place used for exercising horses, therefore a veritable hotbed of tetanic infection . . . and I had nothing with which to treat them All my bottles and instruments were arranged in a neigh boring shack, where I found, after some difficulty, water for washing my hands. Thinking that I might have to give first aid, and, if need be, perform an operation in this poky little room, I was much troubled in mind. I felt paralyzed before I began.

The fencing master watched me curiously. Scrutinizing him in my turn, I guessed that he had never seen such elaborate preparations, and so many instruments displayed, before a duel. I understood his astonishment, and hastened to reassure him.

"I have taken every precaution, and if things come to the worst, I shall be ready for any eventuality. It's all for the good of the fighters. I don't suppose they'll be ripped open, in any event? . . ."

The *maître d'armes* gave me an experienced smile, and added compassionately, "Leave it to me." Meanwhile the last member of the party arrived. . . . But whom do I see? My good friend Jemoli, surgeon emeritus, my professor in operative technique at the university, a specialist in dueling matters. A very worthy colleague. . . . But why has he made no preparations?

I greeted him, and showed him my set-up in the shack. He began to laugh. I felt very much embarrassed, and looked at him questioningly. He took a little case from his pocket, and said, "This is more than enough . . . and we probably won't need it."

I looked at him in amazement. "What? A duel as serious as this? . . ."

"Certainly. The conditions sound bad enough, but there is always an escape. Didn't you read it carefully? A clause empowers the physicians to stop the duel as soon as they find that one of the fighters is in a state of physical inferiority. Just leave it to me."

"All right," I agreed. "We shall see."

Meanwhile, the duelists had stripped to loincloths; the swords were tested; all was ready. The *maître d'armes* gave the signal, and the scuffling began. There was a rain of blows, a din of sabers fending and pointing in all directions.

I stood aloof, as the scene was not to my liking.

My colleague, on the other hand, kept close to the combatants. Holding a big wad of cotton in his hand, he watched them like a hawk. I did not understand at once the reason for his attitude, but a moment later I saw him dart forward, and place the cotton on his client's forearm, crying like a madman: "Halt! He is wounded."

The wounded man had really felt nothing, but Professor Jemoli was so persuasive that the wound *had* to exist. My good colleague flourished the wad of cotton, and cried: "He has a lesion of the dermis and epidermis." He again covered his client's forearm, and retreated with him into the shack. I followed him, and there, away from the glances of the curious, we solemnly dressed the wound. It was little more than a scratch, and though it bled copiously, it was nowhere near a muscle.

The wounded man was as pale as death, and no doubt he thought himself in danger because of the noise the doctor had made. Jemoli disinfected the wound, and bandaged it with so much care that, when the dressing was finished, the poor lawyer looked as though he had just left a hospital. When he stood on the threshold of the shack, the witnesses shuddered. No one entertained the idea, even momentarily, that the duel should continue. There remained

only the police report, and this we filled out on the spot.
It began with the sacramental words:

"Passing, *by chance,* in the neighborhood of the San
Siro race track, we, the undersigned, physicians and surgeons, were urgently called to examine a wounded man,
etc., etc."

But the second duel, at which I had to lend my aid,
was even more amusing.

One May morning, as I was on my way to perform a gastroenterostomy in my pavilion at the Central Hospital,
a messenger came to me with a confidential note. An
immediate answer was expected. I opened the note, and
read. Signor Grandi, an important personage, asked me
to be in the courtyard of the hospital at ten o'clock, and
hold myself at his disposal for some time.

I finished the gastroenterostomy, and went to the spot
named. There I found the writer of the note, who was
awaiting me in a private car. She asked me to accompany
her to a duel at which she was to act as a witness. How
could I say no?

The encounter was fixed for eleven o'clock, at a place
beyond the walls. The conditions were very savage: a duel
with pistols at twenty-five paces, one shot each. I had never
been present at a duel with firearms, but I shuddered at
the idea of a ball in the head or, even worse, in the abdomen. I scarcely had time to get ready. I put the necessary
instruments and dressings in a bag, and rejoined my companion.

The two adversaries were already on the spot, with the
livid faces, restless glances, and impatient gestures that are
quite understandable under such circumstances. I scarcely

had time to deposit my instruments in a neighboring shed—a tumble-down place where every infection, including tetanus, was possible. "Poor surgery," I muttered. "To think that we go to all sorts of trouble to disinfect a wound, and then there are people who do everything. . . ." I was disgusted.

The *maître d'armes* came over and looked at my preparations. I threw him my usual anguished and questioning remark. He seemed thoroughly calm and serene. I looked cautiously around, and asked him a question, fearfully, timidly.

"Don't worry," he murmured mysteriously, "I have done everything to save both their honor and their skin."

"Blank cartridges," I ventured.

"Good Lord, no! I merely loaded the pistols . . . and there is practically no lead in the charge."

I made an appreciative noise.

"And now, Professor," my friend declared energetically, "I'm going to have you measure the distance. Remember—twenty-five paces."

I am quite tall, and my legs are long; under the circumstances, they were still longer. Stilts. My steps were leaps, and such was the distance between them that when the adversaries were in position, they could scarcely see each other.

The shots—one only for each, remember—rang out, and I saw the branches stir above the principals' heads . . . and a few leaves fell. Fortunately, the formidable enemies stoutly held their ground.

They did not shake hands (for all I cared), but they left obviously in a better humor than they had come. I put my instruments, away, thanking my stars that I had not been obliged to use them.

The third and last duel at which I assisted worried me the most.

This time I could not refuse to act, for one of my relatives, a fine fellow and a devoted father, was involved. At any rate, I had the satisfaction of knowing that no one would give him more tender or, I flatter myself, better care; and this conviction helped to silence my questioning conscience. For the third time I was risking both conflict with the law and excommunication. For everyone knows that anyone taking part or co-operating in a duel is subject to legal prosecution and religious excommunication. But it seems that we poor surgeons must get used to risk our lives and health, not to speak of our souls, and usually without remuneration.

However, I am wandering. . . . I could not refuse my dearly beloved relative.

The dueling conditions were very barbarous; the rendez-vous was that same plot of ground at the race track. It was midwinter, and the cold was very severe. I trembled for the poor adversaries: they were both friends of mine—good husbands, good fathers, and both absolute novices at this sort of thing. I shuddered to think of them, stripped to their shorts, facing each other in this subzero weather.

The duel was with sabers, with no strokes barred. There was, of course, the usual clause that allowed the physicians to stop the encounter as soon as one of the fighters was in a state of physical inferiority. This time I assumed the job of spying out the scratch that would allow me to use my authority. I stood as near the duelists as possible, so near that I risked being slashed myself. I had my eyes . . . and my heart . . . glued on those cursed sabers. But there were no wounds, no scratches. My principal attacked like a lion, and his adversary slipped back like an eel. The strokes were fast and furious. . . .

When the referee saw that either was about to be run through, he stopped the battle. Then another bout would ensue—the affair seemed endless. The poor devils were exhausted, covered with sweat. Their faces were livid, congested . . . and the thermometer stood below zero. I forgot the dangers of the duel itself, and began to think fearfully of the possibilities of pulmonary congestion or, worse still, pneumonia. I cursed the inflexibility of that chivalrous code that imperiled such precious lives.

Thrice the duel had to be suspended, and thrice I stirred my principal's sluggish circulation with massage. I myself was in moral and physical pain. The combat, as far as I was concerned, was a moral ordeal that had lasted far too long. My eyes never left the sabers, and my tension of mind was such that I felt faint.

At last, a deep scratch on the adversary's arm. . . . It was bleeding copiously. I darted forward, with the sterilized cotton in my hand. I sponged the wound, crying like one possessed to suspend the duel, and pretended that it was very serious, as I was afraid it might be considered too trivial. I rushed the poor devil into the neighboring hut, and examined the scratch. My colleague assisted me.

It was really a measly little wound. But it was bleeding, and I bandaged it so generously that when I had finished, the poor man looked as though he had been through the World War. And if he was not disabled by the wound, he most certainly was by this unwieldy bandage.

It was decided that the duel could not go on, and the principals seemed quite satisfied with the decision. I suppose they had had enough. . . .

The duel was over, the adversaries made up, and, most marvelous of all, did not contract the slightest cold.

But I swore that I would never act in another duel. And so far I have kept my word.

Chapter XIV

ROMANCE

. . . Quando amore spira . . .
—Dante

Senator Davide Giordano has spoken of surgery in the romance. He has spoken of it so masterfully that I still recall the lecture he gave at Venice, twenty-five years ago, before the Royal Institute of Science, Arts, and Letters.

Davide Giordano was a great surgeon, one of those rare spirits who knew how to blend scientific detachment with a love of arts and letters, thanks to the breadth and profundity of his humanistic culture. No one who heard him could help but admire the logic and lucidity of his thought. At the Florence congress of 1922, after we had listened to learned remarks on duodenal ulcer, Giordano spoke so elegantly, with such critical acumen, and withal so brilliantly that his audience surrendered to enthusiasm.

I also recall the Swiss surgical congress at Lugano, when we were the sole Italian representatives. At a great banquet given by the Società Elvetica, surgeons from all over the world spoke and offered toasts. His Excellency Dr. Motta, the celebrated lawyer then president of the Swiss Republic, also spoke, and, to our delight, in Italian. Davide Giordano returned the compliment in a speech delivered in the purest French, remarkable alike for its ease and the loftiness of its sentiments.

It is rare to find a surgeon who loves and pursues literature. Giordano himself declared ironically, and with his
usual wit, that "literary ambitions are so unbecoming a
surgeon that I knew a man who was eliminated in a competition because one of the judges had said: 'He writes
books that read like novels.' " And Professor Ughetti, who
prudently postponed his novel-writing until he had won the
professorship, says: "The most esteemed surgeon is usually
he who is a bit narrow-minded, who does not boast too
wide a culture, and whose mind is innocent of general
ideas—he, in short, who does not see beyond his bacteria,
or his hyperthermy, or his tympanitic resonance. When the
public sees only these manifestations of his art, so mysterious and difficult, it is convinced that he uses all his resources to probe nature's secrets. On the other hand, it feels
that the surgeon who, besides his science, knows literature
and the arts, writes, and travels, acquires this superfluous
knowledge at the expense of his profession."

Thus Ughetti. Which of them is right: the public that
especially esteems the one-sided surgeons who concentrate
their all on the operative art, or Ughetti, who wrote novels?
I do not know. Possibly a golden mean is desirable, as in all
things. In other words, it is well that a surgeon, in addition
to his profession, should have a general philosophic, literary,
and artistic background, which can do no harm to his full-
flowering scientific activity. However, it is a bit surprising
that a doctor, and particularly a surgeon, should have the
time and inclination to write poems and novels.

I say *surprising*, not *unbecoming*, in this sense: it is rare.
I venture to say that it might be dangerous for a young
surgeon. . . . It is not, however, impossible, for Redi
wrote a poem, and Raiberti excellent poetry and amazing

novels. Mantegazza himself, amid his hygienic researches, found time to write *A Day at Madeira*, which, nevertheless, was not without a scientific purpose.

Senator Giordano has never written romances (that I know of)—he was content to write of surgery in the romances, finding out how novelists spoke of surgery, what conception they had of it, and, above all, how many, and what type of, errors they perpetrated when they spoke of surgery in their writings. He reported some very amusing finds in one of his lectures. For example, De Amacis lets a poor old woman suffer seventeen days with strangulated hernia, and then cures it rapidly with a lightning operation, as soon as her son, having traveled from the Apennines to the Andes, arrives on the scene. Zola has the surgeon Bouroche perform a disarticulation of the shoulder in thirty-five seconds, and in another chapter he has a soldier walk with a bullet in his tibia. The tenderhearted Daudet has a laparotomy performed at a poor devil's *house*, and the technique the surgeon uses is something incredible.

I pass over abortive draughts and descriptions of child-birth and of abortion, whose details are unknown to the most experienced of obstetricians.

Truly, surgery is not the novelists' bread. It is better for them not to speak of it, or, if they must, let them consult a surgeon, and accept his guidance.

But if surgery plays a sorry rôle in the romances, perhaps there is plenty of romance in surgery. For surgeons are not indifferent to women, and they—notably the gynecologists and obstetricians—are strategically situated to win their fair patients' favors.

There is a proverb that applies to these favored colleagues: "Whoever goes to the mill gets sprinkled with flour." The romance usually begins with gratitude, and ends with a sentiment that is deeper, more persistent, more emotional. Sometimes it is a caprice on the patient's part, a little caprice that must be satisfied because it is written: "What a woman wants. . . ." Sometimes gratitude hatches a lusty affair in the style of Boccaccio, sometimes a delicate feeling that breathes the perfume of the violet.

What surgeon has no little adventure to tell, or rather, to hide in the secret places of his memory? Who does not have some cherished memory of youth to recall when his hair is gray? Delicious pages that adorn the book of life, itself so sad and gray.

Well, I too have a story I am tempted to relate, though very softly, *en sourdine* (as the violinists say), as befits whatever evokes the perfume of vanished youth. Do not worry about my wife reading it—she has long known the story and its dénouement. Furthermore, it is an idyll of innocence: a young student's dream. . . .

I was at the beginning of my surgical career when, one day, I received a phone call from a fine hotel. A case of a sprained foot. I was shown into a sumptuous room, all lace and perfume. A young woman was lying on the white-covered bed. She was returning from the concert hall, and had slipped and strained the ankle of her right leg as she was getting out of her carriage. I examined her carefully. Yes, the tibiotarsal joint had been twisted, but there seemed to be no fracture. I applied a temporary dressing, I ordered an X-ray, and arranged for further treatments. My visits lasted for some months, for first there was a period of inactivity, then the series of massages followed by reconstructive treatments which, in various forms, stretched over a considerable length of time. . . . First, injections of iron, then of *forgenina*, then of bioplastine.

The young woman wanted me to spare neither time nor materials, and to tell the truth, it was no unpleasant task. She had so much faith in me, and she was so pretty! . . . Who was she? I hadn't the slightest idea—I hadn't even asked her. A patient, that is all. Once cured, she would probably never see me. again. Quite accidentally, I found that she received letters under the name of Sonia Janowsky. Was it her real name? Her friends called her Princess, but it seems that she had been married to a Polish prince from whom she had been separated after a year.

What was her nationality? She spoke Italian like an Italian, French like a Frenchwoman, German like a German, and English like an Englishwoman. She had arrived in Milan like a falling star, and was interested in music, literature, poetry, and dramatic art. Her conversation was delightful; she spoke gracefully on all subjects, and generally betrayed a wide cultural background. She had traveled in many lands, and knew them well, but she was never loud in her opinions. She led a very retired life, and was in all ways above criticism or suspicion.

She attended only literary and artistic gatherings. She was a splendid young creature: tall, graceful, stately. A queen. She had blue eyes—deep blue, but thoughtful, romantic, dreamy. When she went for a walk, people turned and stared at her. She seemed to say, "Admire me." But when she gazed at you with her blue eyes, she seemed to say, "Love me."

This was what all said of her, but at first I was too busy to see how the land lay. I was about to try for the famous Parravicini Prize, which would allow me to make a pilgrimage abroad, visit the most celebrated clinics, and admire the most noted authorities on surgical technique. My mind and heart were concentrated on this dream. I had no time for other dreams, other enticements.

I won the prize, and my departure put an end to the visits I paid my lovely client.

A month later.

I was at Lausanne, and lodging at a very humble *pension* near the Cantonal Hospital where I frequently attended Roux' clinic. I remained there all morning watching the operations, and at one o'clock I returned to my *pension* for lunch. Even during the meal my head was full of technical methods and operative variants.

One morning the session was particularly long and interesting, and I returned late for lunch. Good old Mme. Lepage, the landlady, was waiting impatiently to give me a package that had come for me by special delivery. It contained a magnificent bouquet of Nice violets, and with them was a very long letter: sixteen pages written in the purest French.

My lovely and mysterious patient, young Mme. Sonia Janowsky, first excused herself for writing in French, but it was the language that seemed to give the sweetest intonation to those three words: "I love you." She repeated them throughout the sixteen pages, analyzing the reasons for her passion. She loved me for (it is her description, not mine) my austerity, my unlimited passion for study, and for my devotion to a humanitarian mission. She admired my will power, my self-sacrificing nature, and my idealistic faith. I was different from any man she had ever known. She wanted to live for me. I had only to call, and she would fly to Lausanne to live with me *forever*. She longed to join her destiny to mine. She would sustain me in life's battles, encourage me, and help me to attain my ideal.

It was enough to make me swoon. I saw this delicious creature, all poetry and delight, walking with me throughout life. I saw her, with her exotic charm, united to a poor, graceless doctor with nothing but work, work, work, ahead of him. It was madness. I closed my eyes, and seemed to see a catastrophe: the ruin of my career, my studies interrupted just when I most needed quiet. I saw economic ruin: all my plans disturbed, my life a wreck. . . .

I had to reply at once, and pray the gentle maiden to tempt me not, to forget me, to leave me to my studies, my hard career, my loneliness, my misery. I had to acknowledge her sweet words, at the same time imploring her not to make me glimpse romantic worlds I could never conquer. I began the letter ten times, but I could write only the most stupid drivel. Ten times I threw down my pen, and destroyed my dangerous avowal. So her letter, romance, poem, remained unanswered.

I gave the violets, which exhaled a perfume that tempted and enervated me, to old Mme. Lepage, who had never seen such lovely ones in so cold a winter. She was *"enchantée,"* and ran off to offer them to the Madonna. . . .

Thus ended my adventure.

I returned to my studies, to my patients, to long and wearisome operatory sessions. For some time, however, I felt dreamy and absent-minded. While I was looking at Roux' magical operations, my mind wandered, and during the recess between the many surgical interventions I would stand and gaze out of the windows of the operating theater. As my eyes rested on the superb chain of the Savoyard Alps, which encircles the azure blue of Lake Geneva, I thought of those eyes, thoughtful, romantic, dreamy. . . .

When I returned to the *pension* for lunch, I scarcely had courage to go in: I was always afraid that she would be there. I knew that if she came, all was lost . . . I would not be able to resist. Those deep, blue eyes never left me at Lausanne, and I saw them mirrored in the ocean's depth when I was going to America. Then the whirlpool of the New World engulfed me . . . and I felt safer.

When I returned, I thought no more of her.

One day I received a postcard from Warsaw, with a date and a signature. It was from her. She said nothing, but I realized that she remembered, and had forgiven my brutal silence. No doubt she thought that surgeons have hearts of stone.

Nothing more.

I went my way, and found every possible recompense in my family. Then came the war. Of my romantic adventure, there remained but a memory.

I do not think that I shall ever see my lady of mystery again, but I have a secret presentiment that she will read these lines. Possibly, after reading them, she may be angry at me.

And rightly so—I should not have revealed such personal memories—I should have kept them locked up in my heart. But I could not resist telling them, for in doing so, they seem to live again. Besides, we are old, and our destinies are so different that they shall never cross again. . . .

On the other hand, the adventure is as fresh and pure as a young student's dream. There is nothing in it to make one blush—it exhales a perfume of roses and violets . . . such as the perfume of those winter violets I received at Lausanne, that cold February morning, and which, in strange contrast, ended up on the altar of the Blessed Virgin.

Chapter XV

THE WAR

The summer of 1914. I was returning home after a difficult operation when I heard, in Milan's central square, a thousand voices announcing, and the headlines of all the newspapers screaming, the beginning of the World War. I shuddered, as did so many others, from tip to toe, and for a moment a vision of disasters, atrocities, and misery passed before my eyes.

After the declaration of neutrality, many people hoped that Italy would keep out of the contest, but the following May it was involved. I had no military obligations, but on presenting myself at the Red Cross, I was attached to an important surgical post at the reserve hospital in Milan. Here they sent those first wounded at the front, and I was able to familiarize myself with the wounds resulting from the horrors of modern warfare.

Nevertheless, the lesions that came to my attention at Red Cross Hospital No. 5, and at other reserve hospitals in Milan, were results of wounds rather than recent wounds. I mean that soldiers, cared for elsewhere, arrived in our hands several weeks after being wounded. First they had received first aid at the front, and then they had been sent to little country hospitals, then to those in cities near the front, and, finally, to Milan after a certain improvement. When they came to us, they were already on the road to recovery.

Wartime surgery might have given better service if it had been developed nearer the fighting zone, possibly behind the trenches. But how could a real surgical branch, a modern service, be organized far from any inhabited center, practically on the field of operations, under artillery fire and in the confusion of a neighborhood so close to the firing line? These problems troubled the heart and mind of every doctor.

They hoped to build portable hospitals equipped with every necessity for performing the most difficult surgical operation, with all types of modern antiseptics and aseptics. This idea was discussed in several surgical centers at the time, and in Milan it won over a brave and persistent exponent in my lamented colleague, Professor Baldo Rossi. Endowed with truly remarkable energy, he immediately received permission to visit the medical outfits at the French and English fronts, and learn the improved methods our allies had evolved out of their already long experience. Thus he was able to create, on these models, complete portable hospitals that could be sent with ease to the immediate neighborhood of the firing line.

Many operative problems were to be solved at these surgical units, especially those concerning the treatment of cavitary wounds of the cranium, backbone, and thorax, and, particularly, those of the abdomen. Abdominal wounds presented a very ticklish problem. It is easy enough to know, after finding that a weapon has penetrated the abdominal cavity, and pierced an organ, that the stomach must be opened, and the lesion treated. It is simple enough to operate when the surgeon has the facilities of a modern and well-equipped hospital and the collaboration of able and experienced assistants. But the thing is not so easy when the wounded man arrives some time after the mishap, in a pitiful state: conditions are unpropitious psychologically as well as materially.

It is one thing to perform a laparotomy in a quiet and comfortable clinic, and another to open the stomach in a tent, with cannons roaring and deathly bombs bursting.

Carrying the wounded man can also be dangerous, for jolting the abdomen may aggravate or widen a localized lesion. For this reason a well-known English surgeon declared, during the Boer War, that if he were wounded in the stomach, he would lie down and remain absolutely still, refusing either to be carried or operated upon.

Furthermore, if a laparotomy is not performed with the most scrupulous and absolute methods of sterilization and disinfection, it can be more harmful than useful. In surgery, more than in medicine, the precept *Saltem non nocere* holds. Furthermore, the problem of abdominal wounds presents wartime difficulties that can be solved only by fulfilling three conditions. The patient must be transported to the operating room in the least injurious way; the operating room must be modern, completely equipped, and near the battle line; third, the medical units must be staffed with able and experienced men.

The medical units were to satisfy the first requirements with automobile ambulances, much more rapid and comfortable than the old military ambulance wagons. The portable hospitals would have to meet the second requirement. The third demanded able and earnest *career* surgeons.

The Italian surgeons were certainly not lacking in willingness to serve. All responded to the call, as I did the first day.

I was soon asked to leave for the front, when the first temporary surgical hospital, called Città di Milano, was organized. I left with my friend and confrere, Dr. Zanuso, with whom I discussed plans. After a brief stop at Vicenza, we were, the next morning, on the way to Marostica, near the Asiago sector, where the ambulance was located. Vicenza was swarming with soldiers, and given over to the excitement natural to a town so near the field of battle. But on the way from the plain to the mountains the signs of war multiplied: long lines of cannons and munition wagons, endless dashing to and fro of automobiles, and columns of marching soldiers.

After Marostica the civil population dwindled: no women or children. The only civilians were men repairing and making roads. Then soldiers, soldiers, and more soldiers—of every service and grade.

The trenches and barbed-wire entanglements began on the crest of the plateau; then the road descended in wide curves, partially concealed from enemy artillery by the branches of trees and earthworks. Here and there, in the middle of forests, were encampments and vehicles, tractors, and mules. On each side of the road were deep pits, like volcanic craters, where the enemy bombs had exploded.

We were now in the battle zone, where deathly shells were falling, and I could see the pains taken to hide munitions, entrenchments, and mounts. We were very near the firing line, as was evidenced by the crosses planted in the earth: the burial place of the fallen. I shivered slightly, and my friend Zanuso compressed his lips. What was the use of talking? It was war.

At noon we reached a little hollow protected by encircling hills, at the bottom of which were numerous en-

campments. Among these were two shacks surrounded by
tents: our hospital.

Weary and apprehensive, we got out. None of our colleagues was there to meet us. Where were our friends?
A soldier pointed to a hut. During the night there had
been an attack on Monte Zebio, and many wounded had
been brought in, including several abdominal cases which
were being operated on. We hurried to the surgical base
which I recall having admired in Milan, in all its shining
newness, before being sent to the front.

Confusion everywhere. Automobile ambulances were
arriving from all sides. Stretcher-bearers were carrying
their ghastly burdens. Cries, curses, and complaints, in infernal heat—it was August 2, under a relentless sun, and in
a cloud of dust and horseflies generously scattered by a
neighboring encampment of mules.

I entered the hut: an oven. . . . I swiftly put on a
blouse, and watched my friends grouped around a cot:
the major was performing a laparotomy. They had been
there since dawn, and showed evident signs of fatigue.
They were at grips with an abdominal wound made by
a rifle shot. A poor *bersagliere*, hit by a bullet the day before, had fallen in front of the barbed-wire entanglements,
and had not been rescued until the middle of the night.
He had been given first aid, and then transported to our
hospital, in what condition it can well be imagined.

I arrived just in time to see the abdominal incision made:
a kind of hara-kiri from the epigastrium to the pubic region. A kind of blackish serosanguineous liquid, mixed with
fecal matter, spurted out. The bullet had perforated the
intestine in a dozen places, crushing or destroying it com-

pletely at various points, after which it buried itself in the
posterior abdominal wall. All the perforations were found,
and assiduously repaired and sutured. They even destroyed
a segment of the small intestine. Then the abdominal cavity
was washed with ether, and drained according to the
Mikulicz method. The operation was performed slowly, but
methodically; the technique was flawless.

The poor surgeons were streaming with sweat; their
faces were congested, almost cyanotic. The very competent
Red Cross nurses were watching . . . almost guarding,
the instruments, as the hut was filled with flies. Think of
the dangers of infection—even of tetanus—to delicate instruments, however carefully boiled and sterilized, that had to
be used on the abdominal organs.

The patient was bandaged and carried out. Would he
live? Possibly. The laparotomy was followed by a similar
case, then by a third, and when I left that hell, I was in a
state of collapse. That night I tossed feverishly on an army
cot that had been set up in an ancient and ramshackle hut.
I could not sleep, for I was not yet used to the faraway
rumble of the cannons and the crackling of the machine
guns. I was enormously tired, but as soon as I tried to sleep,
I remembered the blackish liquid, mixed with blood and
fecal matter, which had gushed from the abdomen . . . I
thought of the injured intestine and of the swarming horseflies, on the lookout for blood. . . .

Then there passed before my eyes those cadaverous faces
of the wounded. I imagined them lying in front of the
barbed-wire entanglements, and waiting and hoping that
when night came the stretcher-bearers would come and
carry them to safety. Suddenly I saw a face that

looked familiar to me, the more I looked at it. . . . My brother? . . .

My brother was actually in a neighboring trench, and several of my cousins were also at the front. "Help!" they were crying in my dream. I awoke with a start, and my nightmare was over.

A stretcher-bearer awakened me early the next morning. Other abdominal cases had arrived: we would have to work in haste. I jumped up eagerly, and hurried to the surgical hut to give the poor devils the fruits of my long experience and ability.

I operated, dressed wounds, bandaged limbs, until I was exhausted, sparing myself for none. I kept seeing the features of my brother, a relative, a friend, and as I shuddered at the ravages of war, I thought of the mothers, wives, and children back home, who were praying for the safety of their loved ones.

A month later, when the temporary surgical hospital was broken up, I stayed on for some time to care for my convalescent abdominal cases. How we worked those weeks! The good surgeons performed prodigies of valuable labor, without stint or complaint. And though they exploited the uttermost resources of surgery, the results were not always what we hoped for. Many of the abdominal cases had arrived at the hospital too late, and in a state that forbade operation. Others were operated on, but the lesions were too severe for any remedy to cure. My first impressions of war terrified me. I was used to emergency surgery in peacetime, to small abdominal wounds made by a knife or a saber or by revolver bullets—mere bagatelles beside the wounds of war. Not a mere gash or perforation, but lesions caused by the bullets of modern rifles or machine guns or, worse still, by grenades or shrapnel. These were not wounds, but devastations. No wonder so many abdominal cases died!

Must the surgeon therefore give up in despair before the great task, and admit himself conquered? Certainly not. Among the many operated on, several had been sent home in good condition, while those who remained were on the road to recovery. I do not recall the percentage of cured to wounded, but however small the percentage and however great our weariness, it was largely compensated for by the fact that we had snatched some of our comrades from the very jaws of death.

As winter approached, hostilities were suspended: the dead season was beginning. Surgical work became rare at the front, and I returned, as did the other career men, to the base hospital, there to care for the men who had survived their wounds. This work was neither tiring, difficult, nor dangerous.

But in the summer of 1917, when fighting was resumed, I was again sent to the front. The temporary hospital Città di Milano was set up on the Isonzo, near the slopes of the Sabotino, by a small cluster of partially destroyed houses known as Quisca. Some of my colleagues had been sent there earlier, and were working in a tunnel close to the trenches, on the right bank of the Isonzo.

I remained at Quisca where I was in charge of cranial and spinal cases. There we treated skull and spinal lesions that had been operated on previously. We kept those so badly wounded that they could not be sent to base hospitals. They were survivors of craniotomy and laminectomy, operations themselves very severe, followed by grave lesions of the encephalon and spinal marrow. Here, again, the wounds were quite different than those I was accustomed to in peacetime. All the lesions were produced by deadly weapons: grenades, machine-gun bullets, shrapnel. Those with superficial wounds—that is, wounds that were not deep enough to affect the nerve centers—were given first aid, and classed as transportable. Only the worst cases remained.

My hospital was full of poor fellows, magnificent young men whose skulls had been fractured by bullets, their meninges injured, and their brains reduced to a pulp. Sometimes the bullet or splinter could be extracted; other times it remained in the cavity. Paralysis or paresis always resulted from such wounds, and usually inflammation of the meninges or encephalon. In spinal cases the bullet was almost always extracted, and even vertebral splinters were removed. When the continuity of the marrow or the nerve centers was affected profoundly—and this is what happened most often—paraplegia ensued, as well as, almost always, paralysis of the bladder and rectum.

Poor victims, doomed to agony in the urinary ducts and to those extensive bedsores, in the region of the sacrum and joints, which were their despair and ours. It was like a nightmare to enter that hut on a warm afternoon. The air would be heavy with a thousand nauseating odors, since it was impossible to renew or disinfect the air. One breathed the stench of feces, stale urine, gangrenous sores. When I arrived, I was greeted by a chorus of prayers, delirious cries, lamentations, and curses.

I still remember a gunner who was hit squarely in the spine. He had the broad shoulders and muscles of a fighter: a colossus so large that he could not fit into the hospital bed. His once powerful lower limbs were flabby and lifeless, as if they did not really belong to him; the bladder was paralyzed, and the constant syringing had produced a painful irritation of the urinary ducts. There was a large fetid sore at the sacrum which was eating the flesh down to the bone.

The colossus looked at me with eyes that would have melted a stone: those eyes seemed to sum up the pain, the despair, the powerlessness of afflicted humanity. And I had to pass through the ranks of these poor fellows a hundred times a day, to comfort them, to persuade them that their torments were going to end, and to assure them that they would return home hale and hearty.

A word about the results of cranial wounds. . . .

A Tuscan peasant was wounded by shrapnel in the left frontoparietal region. He understood and remembered everything, but he could say only one word: the name of his native place: Marradi. And this name he said in every tone, with a thousand inflexions of the voice, in a superhuman effort to make us understand. After which, convinced of his inability, he would burst into tears of despair.

I had to treat others whose occipital lobes had been injured. These retained their intellectual and motor faculties, but they became blind, even though their eyes were clear and healthy. All these horrors were accentuated by the atrocious heat and the endless noise of battle. The attacks on Monte Santo, Monte San Gabriele, and Monte San Daniele went on endlessly, and we were caught between two fires. Powerful batteries had been set up a short distance behind us, and during the night they made a hellish noise. To rest was impossible, to sleep a myth.

Operative work was peculiarly exasperating that season because it was endless. We worked in twelve-hour shifts, but often, after operating all night, we had to take our turn dressing wounds. When did we sleep? When the battle was momentarily suspended! . . . In the meantime, we walked around in a state of vague fatigue, and this indisposition influenced our morale. Some of my colleagues fell sick, and had to be hospitalized; others were thin and pale. But at this time our worst trial was the fact that the morale of our fighters was not what it had been at the beginning of the war.

From what the wounded men said, it was easy to see that most of the soldiers were discouraged. Defeatist and subversive propaganda struck deep roots in this propitious soil.

Our military chaplain heard from the wounded that leaflets inciting the soldiers to revolt had been distributed at the front and even in the trenches. The officers had been warned . . . but would not believe the story. The air was heavy with menace. . . . We were on the eve of the great disaster that still haunts the Italian mind like a nightmare: Caporetto.

The beginning of the spring of 1918 found us on the banks of the Piave.

In the Caporetto disaster, our three fine hospital units had suffered dreadfully. One had been lost completely. Of the other two, the first, after heavy casualties, had been able to reorganize, and set up shop near Bassano; it was under the direction of my friend Baldo Rossi. The other, after wandering here and there over the Venetian plain, established its headquarters near the Piave, between Treviso and the river. Our unit was installed in a magnificent old villa, said to have been built by Doge Tiepolo. The owner, Count Passi, had lent it to the Red Cross.

The dwelling was very fine. Our wounded were installed in large rooms paved with Venetian mosaics, and splendid rooms were reserved for the chief physicians. I could scarcely believe that I had such a grand room to myself, with real furniture and a comfortable bed instead of an army cot. My window gave onto the garden: a veritable park, not very well tended on account of the war, but green and flowery. During the spring and summer the odor of the flowers was intoxicating.

And the company was good. Our chief was Colonel Sironi, a very respected man who came from an old Milanese family. He was kindly and generous, always ready to shoulder the gravest responsibilities. His subordinates were worthy of him—good companions, fine surgeons who were successful in their profession, and held important posts.

After the day's work, we would meet in the ground-floor salon every evening. The frugal meal was like a family reunion. We exchanged views and read letters from our families, but the conversation always ended on the same agonizing theme: how long would the war last?

During clear nights, in order to remind us that the war was still going on, enemy aircraft would pass over, terrorizing the wounded and worrying us, who had them to answer for. The planes came always from the direction of the Piave, and they announced their advent by a rumbling that awakened the heaviest sleepers. As the searchlights swept the sky, the anti-aircraft guns would reply, and soon there was a veritable symphony of whistling and bursting shells and, from time to time, the shattering noise of incendiary bombs. These incursions ravaged the countryside.

Certain sections of Treviso were literally razed, and in the country itself encampments of·sleeping soldiers were singled out. Several bombs had fallen into our garden, and many more on neighboring properties.

I shuddered apprehensively when I thought of what a heavy shell would do if it fell squarely on the old villa, with its crumbling walls and badly repaired roof. I knew only too well of the terror caused by these nightly raids by the invisible enemy. Some of us were too stoical to be impressed by this constant menace. I recall one of my subordinates—a dispenser—who slept peacefully during the most frightful bombardments. Once I asked him how he managed to remain so calm. "My dear major," he replied, "I see no reason to be otherwise. If my time has come, it's no use defending myself. If not—well, no bomb can reach me in my little room." However, my serene dispenser—he was from the South—had adorned his room with charms, horns, nails, and other cabalistic objects.

Once, in the middle of night, a bomb fell on a neighboring encampment of grenadiers. That was a real disaster. Many killed, many more wounded. In the operating room, in artificial light, we had to summon up all our resources to mitigate and repair the hideous ravages caused by this cruelty. And while we worked, the bombs continued to rain down, and the grenades and shells to burst. During intervals of rest I thought of my son, and murmured: "Dear God, preserve my family." Things became calmer with the eagerly awaited dawn. We passed from sleepless nights to days of gnawing fatigue and weariness. We looked at each other over the breakfast table, and thought: "Once more we have escaped."

The spring and part of the summer passed in this fashion,

and life settled down to a sameness: it began to be monotonous. But the Austrian attack in June served to break the boredom. It began about two o'clock in the morning, when we were sound asleep after a very quiet evening. The hideous uproar awakened us with a start. The house was shaking, the windows were trembling, everything seemed topsy-turvy. We all went out onto the terrace facing the Piave. It looked like a monstrous show of fireworks. We heard whistlings, explosions, sinister dronings; the entire plain was alight, burning infernally in a thousand different places.

The bombardment lasted two hours, during which grenades fell on all sides: from the Piave to Treviso the plain was a single volcanic eruption. Then came a sudden lull, and in the distance, near the river, we could hear the crackling of machine guns.

The wounded soon began to pour in. We placed them as best we could—we needed as much operating space as possible. Solaro, Mazzullo, and I used each an operating room, and Colonel Sironi directed and organized the work. For three days and three nights we labored endlessly, desperately, over the most diverse kinds of lesions: abdominal, cranial, spinal, peripheral, not to mention wounds caused by asphyxiant gas.

The wounded painted a vivid picture of the attack. It had been very violent all along the line, and the Austrians, preceded by heavy artillery preparations, had succeeded in crossing the Piave at several places. They had already arrived at our main line of defense, and were still advancing. Between operations we strained our ears: it seemed that the crackling of the machine guns and rifles was closer.

On the third day things went from bad to worse. The

enemy was advancing both to the north and to the south, and we were afraid that we would be trapped in this pincers. A nearby medical unit had been given its orders to fall back, but we had heard nothing. Obviously, in case of retreat, we were to be sacrificed.

Luckily, things changed. On the fourth day a torrential rain flooded the entire region, and for more than forty-eight hours the water fell in buckets. The Piave rose, carried away the bridges, and cut the communications between the Austrian headquarters and the army that had crossed the river. Then it overflowed its banks, and flooded the countryside. Our brave troops, commanded by the Duke of Aosta, held the enemy, and then chased them so energetically toward the river that the Austrian retreat became a rout.

This was the beginning of victory.

When we no longer heard the crackling of machine guns, neither far nor near, neither from north nor south, we realized that the danger was past, and we cried with joy. We acted like madmen, and embraced one another, with the tears running down our cheeks. We were terribly tired, and the work was onerous, for the attack had brought in endless contingents of wounded. But we didn't care. The enemy had been repulsed: we were satisfied.

A fortnight later, we were back to the old tranquil routine. Despite the cataclysm, the countryside was smiling. The garden poured its perfumes into the house, and the birds began to sing. The peasants, who had emigrated during the trouble, returned in a confident mood, and began to busy themselves effacing the traces of war.

During this period, in order to break the monotony, I

visited my brother when circumstances permitted. After long service in the trenches and the breaking up of his corps on the Piave, he was commanding a supporting battalion of the Potenza Brigade in the Monastier region. Seeing him was my only distraction, and whenever I managed to finish the many medications ahead of time, I mounted my bicycle, and was away through the fields. The road was rough and bad. To reach Monastier, I had to ride six or seven miles, and as some of the territory was swept by enemy artillery, there was always danger of intercepting a deadly bit of shrapnel. However, the road was bordered by thick trees, and was so well hidden, that one did not think of the danger.

My brother's camp was far from quiet, and from time to time a grenade would dig a pit in the ground, reminding the soldiers that their lives hung on a thread. They were encamped in open country, between the woods and the marshes on the right bank of the Piave. During the days of June the Duke of Aosta's foot soldiers had performed prodigies of valor here, and all the region, which was also scourged by malaria, bore traces of the dreadful fighting. The encampment lay in this forested land. The only building was a little villa which had been half destroyed by the bombardment, and where the officers dined . . . when they were able. If any friends happened along, they were received with great cordiality, and banqueted in the ramshackle old villa.

I was then a major. My brother, who commanded the post, was only a captain. I was received with all the honors that were due me—I should say my superior rank. But did my presence abash those brave and reckless young men who were used to facing death itself? Not a bit of it. What discussions they engaged in, what conjectures about the future, what criticisms on the conduct of the war! Thanks to this airy conversation, the old villa was transformed, as if by magic, into a noisy hotel dining room. They smoked, and they drank a good Chianti reserved for such occasions.

The mess sergeant organized these functions, but he was very silent, very calm, very modest: he was simply a candidate for a commission, and was acting as battalion adjutant. In this noisy gathering, he did not try to stand out. He remained at the foot of the table, never raised his voice during the discussions, and was primarily concerned with the service. He was, though very young, a married man (unlike the others, who were bachelors). My brother was devoted to him, and often talked with him of his children, his family, and the profession he had abandoned to go to war. He was the communal secretary of a village on the banks of the Tagliamento, that was still in the hands of the enemy on the other side of the Piave. After the war he planned to return to his beloved village, and resume his status.

But fate had another career in store for this guileless young man. His name was Arnoldo Mussolini.

Thus the summer passed, and autumn began. We officers were quite inured to camp life, and were bound now by ties of friendship and affection. Colonel Sironi, our chief, was like a father to us. The days flew by, and winter was approaching.

We were wondering, however, when this life would end. Would there be another winter of war? . . . Everyone felt that things were moving toward a finish. A thousand signs pointed to the fact that after the defeat of June,

Austria would not be able to hold out. The enemy was tired, and his country was torn by hunger and discord. When we launched the offensive of Vittorio Veneto, we were already on the advance. The first Austrian prisoners convinced us that the debacle was inevitable and complete: many of them were exhausted, hungry, demoralized. As soon as they were captured, they asked for bread.

Our unit was waiting the order to leave, and it came one sunshiny October morning. We bade a happy good-by to the old Villa Passi, where we had spent so many memorable hours. We crossed the Piave at Papadopoli, and halted at San Polo where every house was in ruins. We did not know where to go for food. What people we met greeted us warmly, but they themselves were without provisions. The next day we advanced to Oderzo, where the devastation was incredible. In place of the lovely village was nothing but a filthy waste, with a few ruinous houses here and there. Officers though we were, we preferred to sleep on the ground rather than in one of those filthy houses.

To console us for all this dirt, we received the news of decisive victory. It is doubtful whether we, now in the decline of our lives, will ever again witness such intense enthusiasm.

The same day I chanced to discover that my brother's battalion was in a nearby village. I got on my bicycle, and rushed over. But when I arrived, I found the soldiers in a state of the greatest excitement. Hubbub was king, and all were gathered around a wireless station for the latest news. My brother also was as impatient as his men. It was said that our troops had made an unbelievable advance: they had reached Trent on one side, and Trieste on the other. The Austrians' last lines had fallen . . . all was over. . . .

It seemed like a dream, and at first we could not believe it. But the official news came through, and the operator, wild with joy, transmitted it with tears in his eyes. "Austria-Hungary is defeated. . . ." There was a shout of joy; officers and men went wild, embraced, cried. . . . The war had ended with a complete victory.

I left my brother, mounted my trusty bicycle, hoping to be the first to carry the magnificent news to my colleagues. I ate up the few miles between the hospital at Oderzo and my brother's unit, and arrived at my destination with such a look on my face that my friends thought me mad. . . . I was so exhausted by my ride and so paralyzed with emotion that I could not speak. I drew the *communiqué* from my pocket, handed it to Sironi, and gasped, "Look at that, Colonel. Read . . . read! . . ."

There was a second burst of enthusiasm. The news spread like wildfire, and everyone, including our poor invalids, were in the seventh heaven. The war was over.

In the evening, joy knew no bounds. The soldiers could not be held. The reserve stores were opened, eaten, and drunk in honor of the fatherland's victory. Now the nation could fulfill its destiny. . . . This was revenge for Caporetto.

The night was passed in singing: no one wished, or was able, to sleep. The shouts of laughter became louder . . . there was the noise of petards exploding: the soldiers were using as fireworks what had been intended for signals.

The night of November 4, 1918—an unforgettable date.

On the morning of November 5 we left for San Vito on the Tagliamento. We had to halt there for a few days, as sanitary conditions in the region were as bad as could be. The worst contagious diseases were raging in the hospitals: diphtheria, typhus, smallpox, Spanish grippe. The wounded crowded together in the Austrian hospitals were in a pitiable condition. Abandoned for a long time, they were indescribably, pitiably filthy. Medications and other dressing needs were quite defective, and cotton and gauze were completely lacking.

When we had improved sanitary conditions, we advanced to Udine, and then to Gorizia, where our journey ended. Here we remained until Christmas. It was not a very pleasant Christmas, for we were far from children and family, but it brought us the most precious gift in all the world: peace crowned with victory.

Chapter XVI

THE MASSACRE

BUT THE ENTHUSIASM OF VICTORY AND THE JOYS OF PEACE
had but a brief reign. Soon one could sense that all was
not well. . . .

The fatherland, for which we had made so many sacrifices at the front, for which we had fought and suffered,
for which, finally, we had conquered, seemed ready to
tolerate the most disgusting and shameful sights. Our
fighters, wounded and disabled, returned to find the slack-
ers rich, fat, and insolent. If they recalled their daily life
at the front, their suffering, and their deeds, they met
with inattention, boredom, and superior smiles. They had
given up their careers, left their children, shed their blood,
and ruined their health to do their duty, and what recog-
nition had they received?

And now an amnesty had been granted to the deserters.

I shall never forget the shame of seeing our soldiers insulted. One day, as I was rearranging my books, my wife
called me to the window looking out on the Corso Roma:
there was a mob in front of the Teatro Carcano. They
were mocking an officer of *bersiglieri* who had made the
tactical blunder of going out in full uniform, and wearing
all the decorations he had received. The poor fellow finally
escaped his persecutors by taking refuge in the theater.

Strange things were happening. To observe a civic celebration of a patriotic nature I had decorated my balcony, as had been my custom before the war, with the tricolor. I had to remove it because a civic guard ordered me to do so: "It would be construed as a provocation." The public services were in a mess. When I left for the hospital in the morning, I had first to find out whether the streetcars were running. If they *were*, I thanked God: it was the exception.

Idle days exceeded working days, and the strikes tied up all the public services.

In traveling by rail, one could only pray to reach his destination, for if there were a priest or soldier on the train, the engineer might refuse to go ahead. It was dangerous to give an order. . . . Those were the days of the occupation of the factories, of the Red Guards, of the slaughter of Brigadier Ugolini, and of the assassination of the lawyer Giordani at a session of the Bologna municipal council.

Had my abdominal, my cranial, and my spinal cases suffered for an Italy such as this? Had six hundred thousand men sacrificed their lives for such a result?

Here I was living in the midst of all this uproar, and asking myself how it was all going to end. Better to live on the firing line than amid this unleashed madness. . . .

The thing that impressed me most was the massacre at the Teatro Diana. Awakened by the phone ringing at two o'clock in the morning, I heard my colleague, Dr. Meda, ask me to help a family, clients of his, who had been hurt in a horrible disaster, and rushed to the hospital. I was to hurry as fast as I could, so that I could treat their injuries, and decide whether they were to be taken home or to a private hospital. He would be waiting for me at the hospital entrance.

What had happened? Useless to speculate on that. I dressed hurriedly, and soon was en route. A great mob blocked the entranceway. Ambulances were dashing back and forth, and stretcher-bearers and internes mingled with the crowd of anxious-faced spectators, pale and frightened —the hangers-on of irremediable calamity. With some considerable difficulty, I pushed my way, in the semidarkness, through the crowd and the stretchers that cluttered up the door, the vestibule, the corridors. . . .

But what *had* happened? I asked Meda, but he knew little more than I. A bomb had been thrown in the crowded theater, squarely into the pit, and there had been a ghastly loss of life. . . . But there was no time to discuss the matter—we had to find his patients. The rooms, corridors, and wards overflowed with wounded. We scanned every face, and finally, on the first floor, we found the engineer Ventura lying on a cot. We questioned him, but he was too bewildered to answer us. He was torn, dirty, and covered with blood, but except for an injured right foot, which had already been treated, there was nothing wrong with him. Recognizing his doctor, he said with a wisp of a voice: "Don't bother about me—look for my wife and Mrs. Page."

We began searching all over again. Aided by Sister Agostina, we found Mrs. Page, a lovely American woman, who knew not a word of Italian. I questioned her in English, and learned that her right foot was bandaged and bleeding.

"Where is Mrs. Ventura?"

Sister Agostina pointed to a cot. "I think that's she: they brought them in together."

I looked: the woman was half-clothed, wounded, unconscious. Her head was completely swathed in bandages which partly hid her face. Meda raised the bandages, and looked at her. What a state she was in! Her pulse was very feeble, her breath rasping, and blood was trickling from her nose and free ear. She was suffering from a fractured skull, possibly the base of the brain had been fractured. I shook my head: Mrs. Ventura could not be moved, though the other two could. The engineer was taken home; Mrs. Page was removed to a nursing home.

The engineer had been, until then, a happy man: *ein gelungener Mensch*, as the Germans say. Forty years of age, he had had a brilliant career. He was understanding, intelligent, cordial. He held a key position in the electrical industry, and had rapidly acquired a considerable fortune. He had married a fine young woman, and his family life had been further gladdened by two splendid children. That winter he had put through various important deals with a group of American capitalists, and these would stabilize his company, permitting it unequaled opportunities for expansion and development.

Just at that time the General Electric Company of New York had sent one of their big men, Mr. Page, to Milan from Shanghai, where he had managed their electric-light manufactory. Reaching Milan with his wife, he had expedited the business, and, in order to reach a conclusion even more rapidly, had rushed to Turin, that very evening. He was due back in Milan the following morning. His very lovely wife might have remained alone in Milan had not the Venturas, at Page's suggestion, invited her to their home. They had dinner together, and then it was decided to see the popular operetta running at the nearby Teatro Diana.

Mr. Page, knowing that his wife was in good hands, had gone off in high spirits.

The dinner was gay, the conversation good. They drank everyone's health and also to the prosperity of the United States (which at that time had no need of it) and to Italy, which had quite captivated Mrs. Page. At the theater they were enjoying the music when suddenly there was a great commotion, then a frightful explosion, with shrieks of terror piercing the darkness and clouds of dust.

The two women had fainted: they were found in their seats, in a heap of debris, and taken to the hospital.

Poor Mrs. Ventura, the engineer's lovely and accomplished young wife, was in bad shape—it was impossible to move her. She remained on her little hospital bed, amid all that pain and woe.

The engineer, least injured of the three, wanted to go home at once, and so was removed to his apartment in the Via Serbelloni. Despite our precautions against infection of this simple laceration and contusion of the right foot, gas gangrene of the most swift and malignant kind set in. As soon as I saw the way things were going, I consulted my colleague Baldo Rossi, and the right leg was amputated at the hip. But even this did not suffice, and the luckless fellow died without seeing his wife again, without even knowing how and where she was.

The lovely Mrs. Page was also seriously injured. The wounds on her right foot and ankle caused her the most agonizing pain, but her general condition was even worse. She was in a state of torpor from which she roused herself only to cry out for her husband. He returned from Turin the next morning. He rushed from the station to the Grand Hotel where he hoped to find her after her pleasant evening the night before. . . . He met, instead, an employe of the General Electric Company who stammeringly prepared him for the sad news before escorting him to the hospital.

Mr. Page was thunderstruck. He asked us how such things could happen in Italy. He had brought his beloved Eleonora with him from Shanghai, because he had not wished to leave her alone, and now, in Italy—a civilized country—*this* had happened. . . . Perhaps he was cursing Italy in his heart, but his blue eyes carried no reproof. He met me at the hospital, listened to me, saw his wife in the midst of all that misery. He knew that it was better to transfer her to a quieter place, and merely said: "Do your duty."

I did my duty.

We bore poor Eleonora to a nursing home, using all possible care and precautions. The wound was grave: a severe laceration and contusion of the instep, but extremely deep, penetrating to the tibiotarsal joint. We exhausted the resources of surgery, and still the wound grew worse. The fever increased, and we feared that septicemia would set in. Some days later I could not hide my apprehension: we would have to proceed as in the engineer's case. I called Mr. Page, and told him we would have to amputate . . . if it were not already too late. There was not the slightest resentment in his eyes as he murmured, "Do your duty."

I did my duty the second time within forty-eight hours, in the presence of an American surgeon whom the United States ambassador at Paris had sent to Milan in a supervisory capacity. The beautiful leg was amputated. The course of the disease was stormy. Despite the mutilation, infection had encroached upon the lymphatic ducts, and the fever persisted. Of the beautiful Mrs. Page there remained but a skeleton . . . a marred skeleton, at that.

Mr. Page was eager to leave Italy, but he had to await the end of his wife's convalescence. The patient was moved to the Villa Serbelloni at Bellagio, on the shores of the Lake of Como. I had recommended this shelter after the storm, and there, it seemed, they might feel a little less resentful toward Italy. Mr. Page had faith in me, and during their residence at Bellagio, I was often invited to stay with them at the villa. On the eve of their departure, they invited me, with my wife and son, to dinner.

It was a touching evening.

Mrs. Page had regained her strength. It was her custom to rest, during the delightful afternoon hours, in a wicker easychair, and look out on the blue waters of the lake. Did this smiling landscape reconcile her, even slightly, to Italy? Yes, for this stretch of the lake was so beautiful.

She told me that she had seen California when orange and pepper trees were in bloom and the flower-laden Hawaiian Isles; she had been to Ceylon, to Adam's Peak, which has been called the Earthly Paradise, and to Singapore, where the palm trees grow to unbelievable heights. But she had never seen a place so enchanting as this. Mr. Page looked tenderly at his wife: they had no children, and his affection was focused on her.

The next day they would be gone. Their route took them to Varenna, then across the Bernina to Pontrasina, and thence to Paris. After that, America.

They had already expressed their gratitude, but there

still remained something to be said. It seemed either that they did not dare, or did not know, how to express it. So, after dinner, Mr. Page took me for a walk in the garden, along the cypress-bordered lanes. Under the shadow of the ancient trees we advanced toward the mound of earth that alone remained of the old castle. We ascended the platform, and looked, in wonderment, toward the lake. . . . It was Paradise. The Lake of Como lay at our feet, calm and blue, and above it the cliffs of the Grigne were colored by the setting sun.

I looked at Mr. Page—he was in ecstasies. His small, bright blue eyes, now more blue than ever, were fixed in an enraptured gaze. What was he thinking about? Possibly of the verses which begin:

> Far to the right where Apennine ascends
> Bright as the summer, Italy extends. . . .

And finish:

> Could Nature's bounty satisfy the breast,
> The sons of Italy were surely blest. . . .

He must have recalled these last lines, for a bit later he grasped my arm, and said, "You Italians have the most beautiful land, but . . ."

"Yes?"

"You need a man . . ."

"A man?"

"Yes, the right man in the right place."

But there was a man.

My cousin Ernesto Civelli, idealist, patriot, and sentimentalist, brought me the good news. I listened thoughtfully, and he assured me that he had met him, talked to him. There was no doubt: he was a leader. Those who had survived the war—men who had found only indifference and injustice after facing death for their country—gathered around him. Those who loved their country, and refused to hear its name dragged in the mud, flocked to him. The crowd around this teacher of a new religion became larger and larger.

My cousin had read the signs correctly.

In October, 1922, I was in Florence attending a surgical convention. My colleague, Professor Fichera, and I happened to be in the cathedral square when the young Blackshirts were preparing to forge ahead. We looked at each other—events were moving.

The march on Rome came a few days later. The rest is history.

Chapter XVII

THE CONGRESS

I DO NOT SAY THAT GATHERINGS OF SAVANTS HAVE THE IM-portance today they once had (when they were instrumental, as in Italy, of ushering in a period of national revival). But it is certain that in this era of mad intellectual activity it helps students to get together occasionally to exchange the results of research and experience, discussing, criticizing, encouraging, giving battle . . . and, finally, sitting down to a groaning board, adorned with flowers and plentifully supplied with good wine.

Nowadays every branch of medical science holds a congress once a year. General surgery's Società Italiana has its yearly meeting in October, sometimes in one town, sometimes in another. We listen to speeches on subjects that have been decided on in advance, and given to the most capable scientists. The themes, be it understood, are practical ones, and the discussion they provoke are as often unflattering as otherwise.

But it is said that collaboration begets progress, and discussion good feeling.

The congresses interrupt the monotony of work: in short, they give the harassed surgeon a chance for a bit of rest and relaxation. A rested man is always worth more than a tired man. And though the discussions of surgical matters are not always interesting, the rest of the program frequently is: visits to museums and places of historical interest, excursions in the country, and, finally, the farewell dinner.

Some sardonic fellow once observed that these frequently Pantagruelian banquets are in sharp antithesis to science, and especially violate the sane and inflexible principles of hygiene. They can see that the doctors, after preaching sobriety and nonalcoholism to their patients, go from course to course, from lobster to game, all washed down by copious draughts of wine. It matters little that all the witnesses are doctors: if the patients saw these excesses they would echo the words of the German poet: *Was für tolle Sachen auf dieser Welt geschehen*, or the old Latin proverb: *Medice, cura te ipsum*.

Well, happily there are no patients present at these moments of relaxation. Also, the banquet is but the climax of the congress—a mere episode. The one who coddles his own stomach, and does not care to deviate, is free to maintain his sobriety.

The congress itself is a very serious gathering which must occur at stated intervals, just as if it were a religious rite. All surgeons who wish to know last-minute progress in their science must attend. One sees all sorts of people. First, there are the silent ones. Then there are, of course, the chairmen. There are the leaders, those who give the gathering its zip, who seize on the essence of the speeches, discovering the weak point at once, and steering the discussion as they please.

It is a pleasure to hear them. In their audience, apart from those already noted, the ones who sit silently listening and storing up treasures of information, there are, and these are in the majority, those who come one year and stay away the next: the floating members. Sometimes they disappear forever, and their death is announced at the beginning of the congress. The president says a few moving words about the dead.

Every year, unfortunately, there are several funeral orations, during which a shudder runs through the audience. Each thinks that his turn may come next. Possibly when my turn *does* come (and I hope it is many years away), the orator may attribute to me many virtues and talents of which I know nothing. . . .

But a truce to melancholy! . . . When one goes to a congress, he does not want to cry. He wants to recall old times, old associations, with the sacramental words: "Do you remember? . . ." This joyous question usually calls to mind some well-organized, successful congress such as was admittedly that held at Tripoli in 1928.

It was not really a surgical gathering, but a convention called by the government, invitations of which were sent to all professors of medical faculties throughout Italy. Its object was to find out whether Tripoli could, and ought to be, declared a healthy town and winter resort. The guests had to remain in Tripoli five or six days, possibly somewhat longer, in order to judge the climate, but as it was not permissible to hold us any longer than that, the promoters limited our stay to a week, putting at our disposal all means needed for visiting the city, the coast, and the environs.

As soon as I had my invitation from the ministry, with a catalog of all the attractions, I phoned one of my most intimate friends and colleagues, a noted radiologist and incomparable friend.

"Perussia, are you going to Tripoli?" I asked him. "Why not? . . ."

We sent our acceptance. Some days later we left. We went to Rome by night, and arrived at Naples in the afternoon.

There Professor Tandoja, another X-ray expert, who was awaiting his colleague, took us to see the marvels of the Riviera di Chiaia and of Posillipo, not to speak of Palino and Vomero. He was, however, quite abashed. He wanted to show Naples glittering in the sun, and the sky, that day, was overcast. There was a cold breeze from the north that ruffled the usually blue and peaceful waters of the bay.

When the hour for parting came, and we were silent, he thought that we were a bit apprehensive. He asked point-blank, "Do you suffer from seasickness?"

"I hope not," replied Perussia, "but anyhow I have an infallible remedy: Mothersill. It comes from England. My children use it when they feel sick from automobile riding . . . and so I have taken some with me."

Time to embark. The steamer *Garibaldi* was awaiting us.

We found our congressmen and colleagues aboard. They had come from all the universities, but most of them were from Milan. I spare you our greetings, smiles, and jests—even at sea the Milanese is superior in badinage. When four real Milanese meet beyond their city walls, they always find a way of referring boastingly to their origins, and of showing their love for their native place which, as far as renown is concerned, shines throughout Italy. (Need I say that the right ventricle of my heart belongs to Milan?)

The minister had appealed to all the universities, and that which responded most enthusiastically was the youngest, thus following the old and generous Milanese traditions. Milan is the birthplace of many fruitful enterprises, some of which have emigrated for one reason or another, possibly attracted by the magnificence and majesty of the capital. There is an inner logic to events that sometimes causes institutions, like men, to leave the places where they found the best field of activity, and best manifested their strength and ideals. Do you want an example?

Fascism was itself born in Milan, but when it reached maturity it had to march on Rome. Thus we lost the daily presence of the man who conceived and created the great undertaking: the Duce, whom we Milanese are proud to have supported in his darkest hours.

Another exalted personage was born in Milan, and he too went elsewhere. We are very proud of . . . Father Achille Ratti. Under this simple title he had just been named head of the Ambrosian Library. I saw him almost daily, for as a student I haunted this gloomy, book-lined hall. It was warm inside, and there I sat, during the cold winter afternoons, writing my Latin and Italian compositions. I read or wrote, and whenever I glanced up from my work I would see, at his window, Father Ratti, lost amid his books and manuscripts. He was always absorbed, always unconscious of the outer world.

Sometimes, trusting to his amiability, I went to him for information and advice; he helped me with perfect good nature. Once he took me to task for something I really was not responsible for. I had asked the librarian for Carlo Gozzi's memoirs—a book whose light character is not suitable for youthful reading. I had to explain that my Italian teacher had given me a theme to work up from that book. Father Ratti shook his head, and said that the teacher should have chosen something more proper. He ended, however, by giving me the book, along with some good and fatherly advice.

In those days I did not dream that I had received a scolding from the future Pius XI.

I went and admired him when he was preaching at San Giuseppe, a little church frequented by the *Fräuleins* and chambermaids in service with Milanese families. I went often, for his sermons were in German, and this helped me with my German exercises. Thus I had another reason for following the career of this noted scholar who, besides his other gifts, was a polyglot.

One day, his sermon discourses stopped, and I no longer saw him at the Ambrosian. The learned bibliophile had gone to Rome to direct the Vatican Library. We learned soon that he had taken another step: he had gone to Warsaw as papal nuncio. And, at last, he returned to Milan as archbishop.

Once I had the honor of receiving him in my pavilion at the Central Hospital, whence he had come on a pastoral visitation. I cannot properly say how eagerly I escorted him on his tour, stopping at the beds of those who interested him, and asking various details about the patients. I longed to recall my youthful days at the Ambrosian and at San Giuseppe—I longed to recall the scolding he had once given me, and those sermons in the little church behind the savings bank. . . . But I could not overcome my shyness. I am brave to the point of temerity with my patients, but I was unable to say two words to this kindly man, with his encouraging smile.

Today my involuntary German teacher occupies the papal throne, and I am still at the Semeiotica Chirurgica. He is the great Pastor of souls, and I am but the humblest of a vast flock. . . . No doubt, I shall never see him again, but even if I had the chance, I could not summon up the courage to revive youthful memories.

Let us return to the boat going to Tripoli. On the deck, Perussia and I found practically the entire University of Milan. There were so many professors around that it seemed like a session of the faculty. There was the young and elegant Pasini, who had not yet abandoned a certain professional dignity. There was Pepere, always youthful and brilliant, and there Valenti with his wonted aspect of a great lord. And naturally, there was Baslini, by profession an oculist, but in his spare time poet, and bitter critic, and, at all times, a perfect gentleman. Finally, there was Calamida. . . . The whole faculty, in short, but without their gowns, and looking a bit like students on a vacation.

The wind calmed down, the ship put on steam, and night fell on the bay and on Naples itself, which lit its thousands of lamps. The sea was calm, and it was easy enough to sleep. At the break of dawn we were already up, and looking at the marvels around us.

In the limpid transparency of the morning light we could easily make out, on one side, the shores of Stromboli, with its conical volcano, and, on the other, Calabria strongly etched against the horizon. Sicily hove into view, and we entered the Straits of Messina. The unhappy city was still partly in ruins. Etna, green at the base, but capped with snow, was in eruption. We saw Taormina, Acireale,

Catania. In the afternoon we arrived at Catania, where there was a brief stop for a visit to the town.

O Syracuse, city of dreams.

How lovely you were as we entered the port, and saw, from the deck, your shining white row of palaces, and your legendary Fountain of Arethusa, verdant with papyrus! Storied city, city of might . . . though it is said that the present town represents only the ancient Ortygia, a little suburb of the great metropolis which itself extended along the coast and inland, having a circumference of more than twenty-five miles. There, on the gently sloping hills, were the rich quarters of Achradina and Neapoli, of Tyché and Epipolae, now in ruins—very eloquent ruins, however.

The countryside was rich with vegetation and verdure—an intense green, almost brown, but relieved by the yellow oranges; groves and gardens glistening with golden fruit, which, in this flower season, exhale their perfumes over the entire city.

These clouds of perfume are so enervating that they make one drowsy. . . .

There is a legend that, on warm spring nights, a rout of phantom figures penetrates these thickets. . . . Bold horsemen and beautiful girls rise from their graves, and march to the cavern where their king lies buried. In a secret place there is precious treasure. Everybody knows about it, but no one knows exactly where it is concealed. That is why, on warm spring nights, many have tried to follow the procession. They have trailed it into the wood, but not far, because the perfume is so heavy that it puts them to sleep.

We returned to the boat that evening, and once more

advanced through the darkness of the sea . . . and squarely into a squall. We ate quickly, and soon went to bed. But the awakening was far from pleasant. The boat was pitching and rolling under the buffetings of the sea. Through the partitions of the cabins I could hear people sighing—and what sighs they were! Dear old Perussia was not in his usual good humor. Melancholy sat heavily on his brow. He lay on his cot, sad and thoughtful. And to point the irony of it all, those infallible Mothersill powders, of which he had spoke so glowingly, were sitting neglected on the table.

Mothersill, treacherous drug, faithless remedy, graceless specific, had failed. But so, for that matter, had pathological medicine. My friend Cesa Bianchi, the famous clinician, stuck his handsome face out of the bedclothes, but it was eloquent with suffering, not with joy. He was thinking with regret of his dear Perussia. Yes, with regret and chagrin, for he had been unable to rally him, to make him say a word. . . .

They say plenty of bad things about surgery, but if medicine admitted its helplessness in a trivial matter like seasickness, what use was all its study and research among the internal secretions, and among the most profound secrets of endocrinology, not to mention the complicated mechanism of the sympathetic and parasympathetic nervous systems?

Having lost all faith in Mothersill, and disillusioned on the subject of therapeutic medicine, I felt my own serenity deserting me. I felt slightly melancholy. This gloom was contagious . . . it was borne on the wings of those accursed sighs coming through the partition. I dressed hastily, and fled. . . . The keen wind was a tonic: every trace of melancholy vanished. On the deck I found a group of my friends who, impervious to seasickness, were gathered, chatting and laughing, around the prow.

Soon the dinner hour came, and we hurried into the dining room. The tables were almost empty, but among them I chanced to find a businessman, a very old friend, one of those genial Milanese one meets all over the peninsula. He was almost a patient, for I had operated on his wife, the year before, for hepatic concretion. He was a wine merchant, and was making his customary voyage to Tripoli. Business, he admitted, was good. He entertained me with a thousand details about Tripoli, which he knew well, and when he heard that we were going there to study the climate, and to find out whether the place was right for a winter and health resort, he was most enthusiastic.

"A fine idea!" he exclaimed. "It is just the place for a winter resort. France has made Algeria and Tunisia so fashionable that there's no reason we can't imitate her in Tripoli, whose winter is a continual sunlit spring. It's a climate in a million, not counting a few stormy days during the bad season—very few but very disagreeable."

"Suppose we were to arrive during such weather!"

"That would really be funny!" my friend said with a laugh.

The luncheon over, we went up on deck. I joined my high-spirited colleagues. This time, as there was no lady present, the witty Baslini, posing as a fast fellow, was dilating on the Tripolitan belles: splendid creatures, exotic beauties, with black eyes, raven tresses, and sinuous and provocative curves . . . in short, the women of *The Thousand and One Nights.*

The Orient is surrounded by a thousand mysteries, a

thousand legends. I myself knew some of them, and to pass the time I related my own impressions—dating from my travels in Egypt, Syria, and Asia Minor—of the Orient. In those days I was working, during the vacation cruises, as a ship's doctor. I had read Pierre Loti, the fashionable novelist of the time, who had looked at the Orient through, needless to say, the spectacles of his own exuberant imagination. . . . I embarked on the *Regina Margherita.*

The first hitch came at Alexandria . . . the city was infested with cholera, typhus, and the plague.

After health inspection, I was allowed to go on shore. What a disillusionment this was for a poor doctor! The first thing that impressed me was that among the natives few had healthy eyes: many were blind, and a great number suffered from granulation, trachoma, and conjunctivitis of all sorts. The children were bleary-eyed and covered with flies, which they did not even trouble to shoo away.

I visited the Arab quarter whence I escaped shortly, horrified by the filth, skin diseases, and elephantiasis. A regular Pandora's box. . . .

The next day I left for Cairo on a fast and comfortable train, but I found myself opposite a native who, after a time, removed his slippers, crossed his legs, and used his fingernails to investigate the spaces between his toes. Loti had never spoken of that. . . .

At Cairo I found a very modern, very English railway station, from which I boarded a streetcar to go to my hotel. The next day I went to the Pyramids, where a photographer with an ass and a camel, is always on hand to greet visitors. I mounted the camel, and my guide jumped on the ass, the four of us—two men and two beasts—making a very fine group, with the Sphinx and the Pyramids in the background. The pith helmet I wore gave me the appearance of a bold African explorer. The photograph cost a pound sterling: I was assured that I would find the proof waiting for me on returning to Milan.

Suddenly the sun set, and I took a severe chill, as the temperature also dropped quickly. It gets dark so fast that one has no chance to get the least idea of the sunset. Where were those twilights of blood and purple so vaunted by the orientalists? My guide had promised me astounding visions of feminine loveliness that evening, so he took me to the Fish Market—a kind of Oriental ghetto—to see a belly dance. What women! The less said of them the better.

I left some days later, without the least regret. I had never felt the slightest carnal urge . . . but my evening chill was still with me.

I will spare you my impressions of Syria. Beyrouth was quarantined for smallpox, cholera, and plague, and Alexandretta for plague, cholera, and smallpox. . . .

"What's the matter," I asked my audience, "have you had enough?"

There was a chorus of affirmation.

While we were talking, we came in sight of Tripoli. It was evening, and the sea was still agitated, but the port is so fine and roomy that the boat entered in triumph. All the sufferers recovered at once, and as soon as they touched solid earth their gloom vanished as if by magic. But they were all a bit tired, and went at once to their hotels.

The next morning, the congress began. The weather remained foggy, and the wind was up, but Tripoli was lovely anyhow. Here is an Orient that really delights me: it is unprofaned by streetcars and railways. The old city is very fine, with its ramparts, native markets, lanelike streets, mosques, and minarets, not to mention the colorful population. The castle is majestic and picturesque.

The new city owes its splendid appearance to the Italians: the fine shore promenade, the palaces, the stores, the wide streets. In short, everything was tiptop except the weather. I was enthusiastic, despite the rain, but my friend, the wine merchant, was annoyed.

The next day we set out for Sabrata in a fleet of swift and powerful touring cars, over excellent roads, through a picturesque country of oasis, steppe, and desert. At noon we arrived at the ruins of Sabrata, and were served a delicious luncheon on the steps of an amphitheater that resembles the Coliseum.

The next day we went to Garian. After passing through the prosperous plantations, we left Azizia behind us, and so, by steep grade, to the plateau. Here another enchantment awaited us: the almost mythically gigantic olive trees that were said to have been planted by the Romans. Among the olive trees were to be seen villages settled by cave dwellers. Lunch under the trees, and a speedy and picturesque return.

The last excursion was to Homs and Leptis Magna, and was still more beautiful and interesting. We crossed La Menscia, the most picturesque of all the oases, as far as the old mosque of Tagiura, whence, through dunes and plantations, we went on to Homs. But the weather was vile—we were real heroes to risk our skins. The wind was blowing a gale, and the dust and sand sifted through our clothes.

I had gone to Homs not only to visit the ruins of Leptis Magna, but also in the secret hope of keeping a promise

made to my wife: to visit the grave of her brother Mario,
who had perished, at the age of twenty, in the first Libyan
expedition. Hitherto none of the family had been able to
visit it. I naturally wished to conduct my search alone. I left
my confreres at the Casa del Fascio, where they had taken
shelter after luncheon, and set out, following the directions
I had received. A few miles beyond Homs, seaward, I came
upon the little cemetery where the heroes of the Libyan
expedition lie. There I found my brother-in-law's grave.
He is buried where he fell, killed by a bullet in the forehead. He lies between the oasis and the beach, looking
northward, toward his Italian fatherland and the mother
who has been mourning him these many years.

When I returned to the Casa del Fascio, my colleagues
were getting ready to leave for the ruins of Leptis Magna.
But now the weather was relentless: it was almost impossible to stand up, and the sand blowing against our faces
felt like a thousand needles. We managed to see the arch
of Septimius Severus, and to enter the baths, and the little
we saw far exceeded our expectations.

The next day, our last in Tripoli, was given over to
congress business. We had quite forgotten the official aim
of our voyage, but nevertheless we had to meet in the
auditorium of the town hall, and exchange impressions.
Was, or wasn't, Tripoli a health and pleasure resort?

We went solemnly to the meeting. To heighten the
pomp of the occasion, we were to be presented to the
authorities, including Hassun Pasha Caramanli, then syndic
of Tripoli. The Pasha was there, but his bronzed countenance was sullen. Nor was the Pasha very talkative. . . .
Naturally. The foul weather had played him a dirty trick,

and an even worse one on his city of palm trees and oranges . . . which enjoyed eternal spring. All of them were abashed and surly.

We did not know how to begin. . . . But when the dean of Libyan doctors made his clear and concise report, rich in meteorological and climatological data, we congressmen were pleased to state that Tripoli was indeed fit to be considered a health and pleasure resort. I would have added myself that it was a superb tourist center.

After the congress came the inevitable banquet, and then . . . farewell to Tripoli.

The *Garibaldi* was awaiting us, and though a few were reluctant to brave the caprices of the Mediterranean, the return was pleasant. Everyone looked very chipper, and the skies were cloudless. We stopped at Malta, and from there sailed to Syracuse. As soon as the ship entered port, there was a regular epidemic among my colleagues: they wanted to visit Taormina and Messina, and return by rail through Calabria. I stayed on board, and returned to Naples in solitary magnificence.

My train thundered into the old station at Milan. It was a radiant March morning. I found that the city had already donned its spring dress, as if Italy, usually snowy, cold, and foggy at this time of the year, had a malicious desire to prove to the returning congressmen, by the charm of its climate and the gaiety of its sun-swept streets, that it was a splendid health and winter resort.

Chapter XVIII

THE GUARDIAN ANGEL

THE GUARDIAN ANGEL, THE GOOD FAIRY OF HOSPITAL, CLINIC, and nursing home, is still, and always has been, woman: nun, nurse, attendant, *Schwester*. . . . She is the doctor's valued and faithful companion and collaborator, who accompanies him into the hospital, and helps him in his operations, getting the patients ready, and presiding over the instruments and medications. Her assistance is absolutely invaluable.

The surgeon can perform difficult operations, make inspired diagnoses—but he cannot follow his patients every minute of the day.

"Man," declared Professor Varanini, "is not built for these delicate attentions, the loving kindness and care that help sick people along. He even finds it hard to console the patient with a word. This detail work can only be performed by woman, inspired by instinct, delicacy of mind, innate tenderness, and maternal feeling. Woman alone knows, willingly or otherwise, how to inspire or give happiness—she is the eternal comforter of suffering humanity. She alone can find those consoling words and deeds that alleviate the sufferings of mankind."

I agree with Varanini, and add further that though she is immensely important in helping the sick, her services are no less valuable in the operating room, where she prepares the instruments and dressings—work that calls for attention, speed, and patience.

The Americans, who are practical rather than idealistic, regard the nurse's function so highly that they have created a definite type, which is one of the salient features of their surgical establishments. American nurses are recruited from the well-to-do and cultured class, not from the lower orders. They must have a general cultural background as well as a good medical education, the first afforded by primary and secondary schools, the second by the training schools for nurses which are an integral part of every large hospital. I myself have written at length, in various publications, of their three-year course and of the admirable discipline enforced in these schools.

I do not wish to repeat myself, but I am convinced that after this severe regimen the American nurse has a culture and a practical value that is definitely outstanding. Thus she becomes the most active personage in hospital or clinic. Thoroughly capable in the wards and sickrooms, she is equally so in the operating room where, besides preparing, she co-operates. During the operation she hands the instruments and compresses; she even assists directly, and administers the anesthetic. . . . This seems a lot to me, possibly too much. Of course, certain nurses have made a specialty of anesthetics, and thus become true anesthetizers. However, administering the anesthetic is such a delicate operation, and is fraught with so many dangers, that I prefer a doctor to do it.

I have even seen nurses directly assisting very famous American surgeons in their operations. I do not approve of the practice, for a surgeon should employ aides fit to finish or continue the operation if he becomes suddenly indisposed.

In America, in private practice, there is not a reputable

surgeon who hasn't a nurse available during office hours; there is not a well-to-do family which does not employ a nurse to care for its sick. The nurse is highly respected, and, let me add, well paid.

But if the nurse is so valuable an institution, why do we not transplant her everywhere, even into Italy? It is not so easy to answer this question.

I think that the nurse, as she exists in the Anglo-Saxon world, is the product of a wealthy social organism. She could not adapt herself either to the remuneration or treatment our hospital help receive: Italy does not afford circumstances propitious for the exercise of her noble profession. Progress has been made in this direction, but when I began my career hospital service was pitifully inadequate.

In the large hospitals, and especially in the Central Hospital at Milan, they had male help for the men, and female for the women. But these were people with no preparation for their work, being recruited from the humbler and less educated classes.

The male servants recalled the monks in *I Promessi Sposi*: ugly, dirty, often addicted to drink, thirsting for tips, and quick to turn a dishonest penny by the sale of tobacco, sweets, and other contraband—anything to get money. The women, country girls or orphans, were uncultured, sometimes illiterate, always badly paid. They were attached indiscriminately to various services: kitchen, laundry, linen room—and they helped with the patients and dressings.

Only much later did they admit the need of teaching these servants, and at the same time cleanliness was recognized as the *sine qua non* of real service.

Money was, as usual, the stumbling block. The poverty

of the hospitals did not permit them to employ instructed persons of a certain social grade.

Recently the hospitals have established courses in instruction. Girls who wish to follow a hospital career must first shed a few of their country manners, and learn a bit. But they always lack that culture that comes from previous training.

The Central Hospital at Milan supports a school for hospital servants that recalls, on a modest scale, the American training school. Young girls of good family are admitted if they have had secondary schooling. These aspirants are tried out for a time, and, if adaptable, are received into the courses, which include two years of instruction. At the end of the course, there is a practical examination, and the best students get another year of graduate training.

I have followed the development of this school, directed by the noble Maria Sforza, and I have even played a small rôle in its history, being a member of the teaching staff. Difficulties are many, and enmity has not been entirely overcome. But the results obtained have been good, and promise to be better in the near future. Some of our graduates have been worthy of their high mission, and for more than a year my surgical establishment has been staffed by these young women. I only hope that the school will soon supply the needs of the Central Hospital and all the nursing homes in Milan.

Besides this school, there are others in Italy.

Who does not know, for example, the Red Cross school, whose activity was developed during the World War? Then doctors were able to appreciate the great worth of the educated hospital attendant, and I recall enthusiastically the self-sacrificing spirit of those angels of mercy, with their little red-cross badges. They were active not only at the base hospitals, but also at the front, near the firing line, in the portable hospitals. I would like to cite all my helpers, but I can recall only a few names.

At the camp at Mezza Via, on the Asiago plateau, we had General Porro's daughter and the young Marchesa Paolucci de' Calboli. In the inferno at Quisca, on the Sabotino, were the Contessa Buonacossa and Contessa Buonmartini, and Miss Martignoni was for a long time at Carbonera di Piave.

These brave and assiduous helpers, expert in every service, were like mothers to the wounded and disabled. The poor wretches looked on them as sisters, mothers, and comforters, and quite lost their hearts to these patient and devoted women.

Many of the doctors were smitten, and some of them proposed to, and were accepted by, their helpers.

There was my good friend Campagnini, a dauntless surgeon who worked with me at the Red Cross reserve hospital—a man skeptical of, and averse to, the tender emotions of life. But a charming Red Cross nurse won him over. He followed the example of many brave soldiers, disabled, wounded, and blinded, who had married their nurses.

I recall an episode that happened in my reserve hospital, but I do not know what to call it: was it a novel, or a tragedy, or a drama? It was a strange, almost paradoxical affair, and I breathlessly followed its course, a bit remorsefully perhaps, but certainly with astonishment and admiration. I am not telling this story to sadden anyone, but simply to show you what the goodness and devotion of a woman can do.

I was acting as head surgeon at a reserve center—a surgical establishment of great importance specializing in lesions of the nervous system.

One day we received a very grave case—a lieutenant of *bersaglieri*, decorated with several medals for bravery. In his last battle he had led an assault on a trench. The attack succeeded after a fierce struggle, but in the moment of victory the lieutenant had been struck down by a shell hitting him in the back. Carried to a first-aid station by his faithful men, they found that the shell had injured the spinal column at the intersection of thorax and loins. After doing what they could for him, they sent him first to a field unit, then to a surgical hospital. The diagnosis was a bad fracture of the first lumbar vertebra and a lesion of the marrow.

They performed a laminectomy, and extracted the shell, as well as the particles of bone which were crushing the marrow. The continuity of the neural elements had been disturbed, and there was little hope of recovery. But the officer was young and strong, and had passed the first crisis. His lower limbs, however, were flaccid, unfeeling, dead, and the functions of the bladder were imperiled. He was sent elsewhere for a rest, and then to the reserve surgical center at Milan.

When I saw him, I was touched to the quick.

The lower half of his body was dead, and besides that he had great bedsores at the joints and in the sacral region. The intrepid soldier no longer existed—in his place was an invalid doomed to eternal inactivity: a half-corpse. We did everything possible to revivify those dead limbs, using all the resources that mechanotherapy and electricity placed at our disposal. All was in vain. And Lieutenant

Bruno, who was perfectly aware of his sad plight, was in despair.

Was this really his destiny? Was this brilliant officer, the charming young man who had made friends everywhere, the bold engineer who had won his degree *magna cum laude*, and whose future had seemed so bright, to be reduced to feebleness, and condemned to inactivity? Was he, who had been so strong and athletic, to be pushed here and there by wheel chair, an object of pity to the crowd?

Death was better.

I scarcely knew how to act to him: his beautiful black eyes were so eloquent with despair. His glance was frightening. When I was obliged to go into his room, I tried to smile, to encourage him, and to lie about his condition. But sometimes the task was beyond me, and when I left this torture chamber my throat was parched and burning.

"God help me! Tell me a remedy, a way of salvation. . . ."

The remedy came . . . but it was a fatal inspiration.

I asked my young and charming nurse, Miss Nelly, to take care of this hero, to console him, and to look after all his needs. She was ready to perform the noble task, for she was an angel of goodness: calm and serene, as patient as a saint, and very painstaking in her work. She had taken up nursing against her parents' wishes. Now, after a life of ease in the bosom of a noble family, she served humbly, enthusiastically, performing the hardest and most disagreeable tasks.

Miss Nelly performed the miracle.

She tended Lieutenant Bruno affectionately, tenderly, with exquisite delicacy. She cheered him up, and told him stories; she read to him, and amused him. And we saw a change come over our obstreperous hero. His wrinkles vanished, and there was a look of resignation in his eyes. He had his moments of despair, but as soon as Miss Nelly entered his room, the clouds disappeared. He considered her a goddess . . . he looked at her with ecstasy.

He was much better in every way, and a few months later I declared him fit to be sent elsewhere for convalescence. Surgery had done for him everything in its power, but no human agency could ever give him the use of his legs.

He left, his wheel chair propelled by the faithful little nurse. . . .

Miss Nelly asked for a few months' leave of absence, which I was happy to grant, seeing that she had performed prodigies of work.

A few days later I was in my office when I was told that a lady wished to see me at once. It was Miss Nelly's mother, whom I had known for a long time. She entered hurriedly, threw herself into an armchair, and burst into tears.

"Doctor," she stammered through her tears, "my Nelly . . . my poor dear Nelly. . . ."

"Well, is she ill?"

"No. It's much worse than that. She's engaged."

And she burst into a fresh fit of sobbing.

"Well, that doesn't sound so terrible."

"You think not? . . . But listen. . . . She wants to marry Lieutenant Bruno."

It was my turn to collapse in my chair. Did this young woman, brimming over with youth and health, wish to marry a poor invalid—a paralytic? . . . Such a thing must not be allowed: it was a crime against nature, against motherhood, against procreation.

I calmed the distracted mother, and promised to try to dissuade the obstinate Nelly.

I called on Lieutenant Bruno, and tactfully appealed to his generosity and self-abnegation. Then I spoke to the young girl both as her physician and her superior. I pointed out to her the enormity of her sacrifice, the grief of her parents, the irreparable damage she would be doing.

All was useless.

She merely replied that without her, Bruno could not live, and that he would die of despair. He had sacrificed his life for the fatherland—it was only right that she should sweeten and ease the hero's life.

The inconsolable family absolutely vetoed the marriage, but Nelly was of age, and the marriage took place a few months later. One gray morning in April, the invalid was wheeled to the altar, and the two young people pronounced the fatal yes.

The relatives and friends hadn't the heart to be present.

Now, in his own house, Nelly surrounded Bruno with love, tenderness, and constant care. I had not the courage to visit them, but sometimes I met them on the street. An attendant was pushing the wheel chair. Bruno's face was changed, almost radiant. Nelly walked beside the chair, looking at him affectionately, almost maternally.

But one day the lieutenant had a relapse. His bladder troubles reappeared, accompanied by a violent infection of the urinary ducts. The young hero died resigned, blessing the woman who had shared his sufferings and sacrifice. The virgin wife kissed his dying lips, and swore she would never love another man.

The poor body, which had actually been dead for so long a time, was dressed in its glorious gray uniform.

Miss Nelly's task was done.

She put on mourning, and returned to her family, to devote the rest of her life to works of charity.

So ends the pitiful story of the sweet and heroic little nurse: the small white figure with her red cross. I admit that her generous nature may seem exaggerated, disconcerting, almost unnatural. But we men cannot understand. The heart of woman has many secret chambers, many deep and unfathomable abysses that we are not allowed to penetrate.

We can only admire. . . .

Chapter XIX

THE MARTYR

TO MY FATHER

ALFRED DE MUSSET WANTED HIS FRIENDS TO PLANT A MEL-ancholy weeping willow over his grave:

> *Mes chers amis, quand je mourrai*
> *Plantez un saule au cimetière. . . .*

A tribute of palm leaves belongs on the grave of the surgeon who has died in line of duty. For the willow symbolizes only pain, while the palm is the martyr's attribute.

Poems do not kill the poet, and if they are inspired, they give him immortality. The practice of surgery, however, entails constant danger, without hope of glory, and most often gives no reward but obscurity and humbleness. The surgeon is always on the breech: his hands touch the most nauseous sores, and are exposed to the most infectious exhalations and the most virulent secretions.

He must treat and operate in cases of tumor, tetanus, carbuncles, erysipelas, diphtheria, and so on, and woe to him who relaxes disinfection, if only for an instant. Woe unto him who cures others, but forgets himself.

I had a terrible example of professional misfortune in my own family: my poor father, as I have said, contracted septicemia while performing an autopsy, and died some days later. A very slight unnoticed scratch gave entrance to the disease germs.

261

Many surgeons have suffered the same fate in operating on infected patients.

The methodical use of rubber gloves has much diminished the number of these catastrophes, but has not done away with them completely. While operating, the surgeon can always prick himself accidentally, thus injecting disease germs into his own flesh. Such accidents have occurred recently to some of my colleagues. I myself have twice had such an experience, having been infected by pus germs. Twice my poor hands were under the surgical knife, and my family was gravely alarmed. Fortunately, the danger passed quickly because of the timely surgical intervention, but several of my colleagues were not so lucky.

I recall a terrible infection of the middle finger of the right hand that my old teacher, Professor Bussola, contracted while operating on an ulcer on the arm of a hospital patient. It is truly miraculous that the life of the wretched man was spared. For weeks his robust constitution fought against death, and he was saved only by the amputation of all three phalanges and the metacarpus. I need not mention the professional damage due to this mishap.

The same misfortune happened to my friend, Colonel Sironi, as well as to Dr. Boni. The lamented Professor Crosti contracted the erysipelas that caused his death, and my colleague, Dr. Radice, barely escaped blindness when a jet of pus from a pleuritic ulcer he was operating on, struck him in the eye.

And I could cite any number of cases, were I not afraid of being tedious.

But syphilis is unquestionably the worst infection. It is

the surgeon's nightmare—this direful malady which, with its strange and protean manifestations, attacks man in his most vulnerable spot: his children.

The germs of this disease do not infect anyone with a thoroughly sound skin, but if, either on the flesh or mucous membrane, there is a break in continuity—a wound or even a slight scratch, then the fatal spirochete enters and worms its way into the tissues. There it flourishes and multiplies, giving rise to the manifestations of primary syphilis: a tiny callosity which sometimes passes unnoticed. But now the spirochete invades the entire organism.

So we pass on to the secondary stage, when the manifestations are not confined to the point of entry, but are diffused. They become visible particularly on the skin and mucous membrane. There is a rash: scabs and pimples on the mouth and lips, and, most noticeably, on the genitals. The secondary stage lasts two or three years: it is the most dangerous, the most contagious, because the manifestations are superficial, though obvious. This is the period when the syphilitic baby infects the nipples of his nurse's breast, and the woman in turn spreads disease with her kisses and in the sexual embrace. In this case, though syphilis is classed among the venereal diseases, the description is far from exact.

After the secondary stage, the superficial manifestations disappear, and serious visceral lesions follow: the spirochete attacks the most vital organs—the heart, the vessels, the sexual glands, the nerve centers. This tertiary stage can last, if not treated, throughout life. The disease is not so contagious, but it is more harmful to the patient, for the cardiac lesions cause sudden death, and the vascular ones arthritis and aneurism. Those of the sexual glands allow the disease to be transmitted to the children, and those of the nerves cause dorsal phthisis and insanity.

Can such a disease be cured?

Yes, it can be cured, and cured well, completely, basically. But the treatment takes a long time, and involves patience, persistence, and perseverance. Then it can be cured, though there are possibilities of reinfection.

The methods used against syphilis are truly miraculous. We have at our disposal remedies that are quite as wonderful and efficacious as those used against tuberculosis, and much better than those used against malignant tumors and, particularly, cancer. With the aid of certain drugs, even the gravest manifestations of the disease can be quickly exorcised. The patient regains—or seems to regain—his health, and he is apt to think himself completely cured. There lies the danger: discontinuing the treatments.

Then the reckless fellow inadvisedly marries and begets diseased children. Some years later, just when he least expects it, the symptoms reappear and attack the organs that have been most strained and fatigued during his life.

Among intellectuals the brain runs the greatest risk. Many fine men of letters and artists die of general paralysis at an early age. Take Donizetti, for instance, who spent his last years in an asylum at Bergamo, after writing his delightful operas.

But I am getting into a field of action where my friend Pasini reigns supreme.

I must explain this little digression because I have always had a holy horror of this disease. I assure you, confidentially, that, considering the many risks I have run, it is a miracle that I have escaped it. I have wounded or pricked myself countless times while operating. During the war, while the disease was rife among the soldiers, at a time when we were beside ourselves with work and emotion, we had little time for precautions. Doubtless I operated on many syphilitics without knowing it, and doubtless I pricked myself while I was operating on them. All my colleagues were not as lucky as I. Many were struck down while doing their duty.

I remember the long and painful odyssey of a celebrated professor of obstetrics in one of the royal universities. This noted scientist pricked his finger while he was performing an autopsy on a fetus. It was so malignant an infection that it could not be cured completely, and some years later appeared the first symptoms of dorsal phthisis. Between attacks of shooting pains he was wheeled to his lecture room, where he remained for many hours talking with his students. He stuck to his clinic until his last hour—"the conqueror and not the conquered, triumphant over his suffering and pain." When he was advised to give up teaching, and take care of himself, he replied: "Only when I speak to my students can I forget my pain—only then do I regain my strength, and forget the horror of my nights of sleeplessness."

I saw some contract the hideous disease under my very eyes. A celebrated Milanese obstetrician, now dead, infected his finger during a gynecological operation. And many others were infected while doing their duty. I cannot speak of all the dramas of this sort, since professional secrecy forbids my citing these heroes by name. Obscure, shadowy figures—benefactors whose sacrifice was not allayed by gratitude.

But I must pass on to one sad story, told me by my colleague Smidt at an international surgical convention. Let him tell it in his own words:

"My dear Majocchi, surgeons make the worst patients. They cure others, but when they themselves are ill, they are truly pitiable.

"This year I lost my most cherished assistant because of a professional accident. The case was serious from the start, but no one can persuade me that, had he only used patience and perseverance, he would not have escaped a painful death. If, instead of being an intelligent and cultivated doctor, he had been an ignorant layman, he might perhaps have been cured.

"Even as a student, Dr. Braun was mad about surgery, and after taking his degree he still accompanied me to the hospitals. He was terrifically energetic, always ready for work. Between operations, during his free nights, he read books, journals, scientific papers. He was a man of solid culture, and would have arrived quickly at the top. After a year he was already assistant at the hospital. He was a professor after three years, and a year later he married. I was his witness. He was soon the father of a little girl . . . and then the war came to disturb this idyll. For some years I lost sight of him.

"He was attached to the surgical branch in one of the reserve hospitals, and in his free time he carried on his private practice. He was already highly respected, and well on the way to acquiring a very profitable clientele.

"One morning he walked into my dispensary: his hand was bandaged.

" 'What has happened to you, my child?'

" 'Professor, please give me your opinion. Look at the index finger of my left hand. I pricked it while I was operating . . . I do not remember exactly when. Probably it was at the military hospital . . . I don't know. At the moment, I paid no attention to it. Then it swelled slightly, and I used poultices on it. I showed it to a colleague who said it was periungual whitlow, and opened it for me. But that did not cure it, that will never cure it . . . and I must work. . . .'

"I took off the bandage, and looked at the index finger. It had a small granulous sore, gray, strange-looking. But it did not suppurate—it was not even very painful. He also had large pimples on his armpit, but they, too, were not painful.

"I hesitated, prescribed more poultices, and asked him to return in a few days. He came. This time I had an expert on syphilis with me. There was a horrible doubt in my mind, and I wanted to share the responsibility with someone. Above all, I wanted a microscopic examination. Poor Braun read the anxiety in my eyes. And it was as I had feared: the microscope revealed the spirochete in the depths of the wound. It was syphilis.

"My poor assistant collapsed into an armchair, and burst into tears of anguish.

"He had dreaded venereal disease, had passed his hard-working youth in chastity, and had married without fear of transmitting anything but his own fine health to his children . . . and now he was a syphilitic, infected. He would not be able to approach his wife, he would not be able to kiss his little girl. . . .

"I comforted him as well as I could. He had to take good care of himself, and with patience he would be cured. He would have only a memory of the professional mishap. . . . I accompanied Braun home . . . all the life had gone out of him. Fortunately, his wife was a truly superior woman: she understood the situation, and rose above it. She instituted a strict hygienic regimen: she separated the beds, the linen, the eating utensils. And, above all, she comforted her discouraged husband.

"Braun responded at once to the energetic treatment. After the first injections, the symptoms vanished. The ulcered finger was cured, as if by magic, and healed in a few days—the secondary stage was averted. Braun was improved in body and soul. It was a bore to conform to all the restrictions, and it was torture not to be able to embrace his wife. Worst of all, he couldn't kiss his little daughter, who thought her daddy was angry at her.

"He left for the front, and I accompanied him to the station. I said good-by to him, and then added a final word: 'Braun, don't forget to continue the treatment. Remember the watchword: perseverance, patience, tenacity. . . .'

"He promised me, and the train left.

"I got many letters and postcards from him, describing the life at the front, the details of his immense surgical experience with the wounded. But he did not speak of himself. He seemed to have forgotten his health for that of others. There was a secret doubt gnawing at my mind: I had a sad presentiment. . . . Would he take care of himself?

"Two years passed. The war ended, and Braun returned to the hospital. It was Braun of the old days—he even seemed younger. He resumed his work and scientific researches with extraordinary enthusiasm. To operate with him was a pleasure. I did not have to say a word: he anticipated my wants, and satisfied them promptly, calmly. When I cut the tissues, I had no time to perform the hemo-

stasis. In a twinkling of an eye he had ligatured all the
vascular openings. When I was in doubt I asked his opinion,
and his advice was always wise and cautious.

" 'Braun, are you leaving a drain?'

" 'Braun, ought we to close it completely?'

"But he worked himself too hard—I had noticed it several times. He devoted the day to his patients, and at night
he retired to his study to write. He was making a name for
himself. . . . But I was worried about his health.

" 'Braun, are you continuing your treatment?'

"He reddened like a schoolboy, and replied: 'I had many
injections at the front, and then I had a blood test. The
Wassermann is negative.'

" 'Braun, my friend, don't rely on the Wassermann—
it is not infallible. Go on with the treatment.'

"He did not reply—he seemed put out. Possibly my
words had recalled painful memories to his mind. It was a
closed book he did not wish to reopen.

"In the meantime, years were passing, ten since his infection. Braun was now a successful surgeon—a man to be
reckoned with. But one day something happened that froze
the blood in my veins. He was assisting me in an operation
for fibroma. A seton got loose, and blood jetted out—the
vascular opening yawned before our eyes . . . and Braun
did not know how to seize it. He was brandishing the hemostatic forceps in a perplexing manner, unable to find what
he was looking for. I glanced at him in amazement: he
blushed, and looked embarrassed.

"Some days later I had an even more painful surprise.
I was at the window of the surgical building when I saw
Braun arrive. He was violently agitated: he was gesturing
and talking to himself. A bit later I heard an unusual noise

in the ground-floor ward. I went downstairs. I could hear Braun's voice very clearly, but it was distorted by wrath: he was attacking the patients, scolding them incoherently. Then he saw me, and tried to calm down. I invited him into my study.

" 'Listen here, old fellow,' I suggested, 'why not take a rest for a few days? You have been working too hard.'

"But he turned his back, and stalked out of the room, muttering defiantly. He was no longer the faithful assistant and friend. . . . There was no doubt. These were the first symptoms of progressive paralysis.

"The next day Mrs. Braun came to see me. Her husband had abused her . . . it was a wonder he hadn't struck the child. He had risen during the night, and had run through the apartment, crying that he meant to chase out the evil spirits. He had put the house topsy-turvy, and at last a kindly neighbor had gone to fetch the police. They had come and taken him away to an asylum.

"The poor woman begged me to use every possible means, every scrap of my influence, to have Braun removed from the horrible place, and taken to a nursing home. It was done, but in the nursing home the tragedy began all over again. There they tested both his blood and urine, and in both cases the Wassermann was positive. An energetic antisyphilitic treatment was undertaken at once, but without result. It was too late. They tried maleriotherapy, and induced a fever that almost endangered the patient's life. There was a slight improvement, then a relapse.

"We were in despair. I went often to see him, but these visits were pure torture. Sometimes he recognized me, sometimes not, but the gaps in his memory were always frightening. He suffered from persecution delusions: everybody was plotting against his career, and now they had shut him up in prison because they wanted him to die. His room was invaded by evil spirits, and in order to defend himself against them he had covered its walls with holy images of a frighteningly childish nature.

"This lasted for some months. Then came insanity.

"We had to witness the decline of this magnificent mind, of this energetic man who should properly have been at his prime. Fortunately he had a sharp attack of pneumonia, and after a few days died in delirium. He could not recognize his wife or daughter. . . . But almost until he breathed his last, he twirled the index finger of his right hand—the finger which bore the little white scar, the reminder of that slight prick through which infection had entered his body, while he was doing his duty as a surgeon.

"O Braun, my child, *Mein lieber Sohn! . . .*"

Professor Smidt was deeply disturbed, and could say no more. I silently left the room—I had to have air: I was suffocating. I wandered through the streets, trying to get the story off my mind. But I couldn't: that sad and raucous voice kept repeating stubbornly: "O Braun, my child, *Mein lieber Sohn! . . .*"

This cry seemed to overwhelm everything, like the rising tide . . . I seemed to hear all the victims of the surgical art. I thought of my father dying of septicemia. I seemed to see him on his bed of pain and death, and to hear the sobbing of his wife and children.

I also saw the poor professor of obstetrics in his wheel

chair, talking to his students in the lecture room, the only place where he could forget his grief and pain.

I saw the maimed hands of my colleagues. . . . And then I saw the long line of the unhappy men, young and old, known and unknown, famous and obscure, who had given their lives to surgery: the martyrs of my profession.

Chapter XX

DIAGNOSES

THE DOCTOR WHO PREPARES TO TREAT A DISEASE MUST FIRST understand the nature of the changes he hopes to remedy. He cannot undertake a treatment without having an exact knowledge of the disease. To gain such knowledge he must observe and study his patient.

There is no disease that does not reveal itself, at the very beginning, by a certain number of anatomical and functional changes. These symptoms (*ta semeia*, the Greeks called them, whence the term semeiology for the science that has to do with the investigation of symptoms) furnish the data from which the surgeon must deduce the conclusion that is known as the diagnosis.

But finding out these manifestations, or symptoms, which constitute the first step, if not the basis of all therapy, is not always so easy. There are some very clear, very easily observable signs. There exist others which require special education of the senses. And there are some which are brought to light only by the use of fine and delicate instruments.

As an example, an attack of appendicitis is accompanied by pain, swelling, and change of blood. The pain is apparent: the patient himself can describe it. The swelling is not always evident; sometimes it is very slight, and may even require a peculiar delicacy of touch to detect it. The change of blood requires, to be evidenced, a very fine detecting instrument. Each of these symptoms must be grasped by the surgeon, but each demands a certain praxis, a special technique that long experience alone can bring.

The art of finding and recognizing these various symptoms constitutes the first step in practical surgery. To borrow the words of the famous Alessandri, it is the clinical key, the base, the foundation of the entire surgical edifice. The teaching of this discipline, acquiring an ever increasing importance in the modern university schools, is known as semeiotics: the technique of deducing diseases from their symptoms. In spite of many difficulties, the University of Milan has created a special chair in semeiology.

When I assumed the chair, I was head surgeon in the large surgical wing, which thus automatically became known as the clinic of surgical semeiology. The pavilion, already rich in apparatus, though completely lacking in facilities for teaching, had to be adapted to its new rôle. There were neither lecture rooms nor laboratories. A real center for surgical diagnostics was needed, but how could we bring it into being? I could count only on private generosity, and fortunately the great heart of Milan was not found wanting.

It so happened that I was called to attend one of my cousins, who had been injured in a grave accident. As he had broken one of his lower limbs, the patient was bedridden for a considerable length of time. He received daily, as is usual in such cases, a number of his friends, who came to keep him company. I occasionally stayed to gossip, and one day the conversation turned on education. I explained how much difficulty I was having in my course, especially because of the need for a laboratory. My words were listened to attentively, and as I sowed I reaped.

Some days later the patient announced that one of my hearers offered to donate all that was needed to start the clinic under the very best conditions: lecture rooms and laboratories stocked with instruments. The necessary sum was offered simply and with absolute spontaneity. I remember the donor's annoyance when the hospital executives published, as is customary, his name and deed. We had to insist that the clinic bear his name, for the generous Enrico Borghi wished to remain anonymous. He was only interested in one thing: the clinic's usefulness to science and surgical instruction.

The school of surgical diagnostics has been functioning for more than seven years.

The investigation of symptoms is the basis and first principle of surgical treatment: it is the first step in therapy. It ennobles operative art which, without clinical investigation, would be nothing but manual labor, like the work of the barber-surgeons in the Middle Ages—a decay of an art which, according to old Hippocrates, could only be ennobled through the delicate touch of diagnostics.

But the story of diagnostics teems both with triumphs and mistakes. It can be a source of unhappiness to the patient who finds that he is suffering from a disease no human power can alleviate or cure. Physicians must often have the same experience when they are ill.

Laymen are generally sheltered from the truth, for their doctors strain their ingenuity to conceal the painful results of a horrible diagnosis. Thus the patient owes to his physician the advantage of arriving at death's door without knowing it. The surgeon often plays the same rôle, for the patient's fears are frequently staved off with the pious cliché—"The illness is long and wearisome, but susceptible to treatment."

There is none as blind as he who does not wish to see.

But when a surgeon or doctor undergoes treatment, that is another matter. There are certain facts that are absolutely incredible. I have seen learned clinicians, almost infallible diagnosticians, be completely wrong about themselves. These are able and experienced men, who ordinarily can diagnose any disease in the twinkling of an eye. And yet they make the most absurd mistakes when they themselves are involved.

I remember the case of one of the most learned surgeons I have ever known. He was one of my colleagues. Having won a prize that permitted him to take graduate work abroad, he returned, after a long absence, with such a magnificent technique that he soon won general esteem. A short time afterwards, he was stricken by pulmonary tuberculosis. From the beginning the symptoms of the fatal disease had been obvious, but he did not suspect the truth. None of his colleagues had the heart to drive him from his fool's paradise. I even think that even if irrefutable proofs had been shown him, he would not have believed: he would have taken us for visionaries. And yet one only had to examine his spittle under the microscope to realize the truth.

The poor wretch even had the audacity to marry and beget children. Once my friend Lorini, of the old Obstetrical Station, was summoned to attend his wife during pregnancy. She was in danger of uterine inertia. While Lorini was using his forceps to bring a sickly child into the world, the wretched father was shuddering in an access of fever. He was still insisting, as he had insisted always, that he suffered from a stubborn malaria, accompanied by daily fever. But with a little patience and perseverance he would master it.

But that is not the rule. The doctor is often the first to face the facts. His coldly logical mind does not shrink from the specter summoned up by the diagnosis, and gives way to despair only when he realizes that the battle is lost.

My beloved friend and second father, Dr. Ferri, told me a very sad story about one of his colleagues, a man with whom he had shared professional troubles and daily cares. He was one of the head men at the Obstetrical Station, and was noted for his competence and energy alike. He had always gone out of his way to assuage the sufferings of others, and now, one mournful day, he saw that he was in a worse spot than his patients. He had pulmonary tuberculosis.

He was mistaken at first, but the pitiless lens of the microscope had revealed the presence of Koch's bacilli. He began a strenuous course of treatments, with all the energy of a drowning man clutching a straw. But the disease was stronger than the remedies. There was no hope, no possibility of being saved.

One sad winter morning he surrendered to despair, and took a tablet of potassium cyanide. He figured that death would come quickly, but the reality was different. He vomited up the poison, fainted, and lay gasping for breath. The servants, finding him lying unconscious on the bed, phoned his faithful friend.

"I hurried over as fast I could," Ferri said, "for I had had a presentiment for some time. I rushed upstairs, and burst into the room which was filled with the strong odor of bitter almonds characteristic of hydrocyanic acid. There lay my dear old friend, his lips blue, respiration scarcely perceptible, and eyes rolling in their sockets. There was a slight foam on his lips. I pounced on the dying man, and began vigorously to chafe his wrists. I continued artificial respiration until I was exhausted. In a half-hour he regained consciousness. He looked at me amazedly, even with a kind of terror. He was still living . . . it seemed incredible to him. He seemed to say, 'Not even death is kind to me.'

"I continued first aid until he was out of danger. My patient looked fixedly at me, as if he wished to say something, but could not. Then he signed for me to come near, and then he whispered these heartbreaking words: 'Attilio, my dear friend . . . I should thank you. . . . But should I? You have been good, but why have you been?' He had a violent fit of coughing, and I had to raise his head from the pillows: he seemed to be suffocating. He calmed himself, and resumed: 'Why did you save me? Now I shall have to die all over again. . . . Listen, Ferri, you know there is no hope for me. I have known the exact diagnosis for a long time . . . and it is horrible. If you only knew how often I have envied our patients who die without knowing what ails them!

" 'Listen, Ferri,' he began again after another fit of coughing, 'if you had a sick dog, condemned to die as I am, wouldn't you put it out of its misery? Why let *me* suffer? Why must I continue to live in torture? What good is it? I have no family, I am alone in the world. . . . Why prolong the agony? Attilio, my friend, why did you save me?'

"This time he hadn't the strength to continue, and the trembling words ended in such an exhausting fit of tears that he fell into a highly opportune sleep. I watched at his bedside, and when he awoke he had recovered completely from the ill effects of the poison. He thanked me, and promised that he would never again attempt suicide while he was still able to work at the hospital.

"He was a brave fellow. He returned to his duties, and for several weeks appeared at his building at the usual hour. I watched for him every day, wondering just how long this sad life would continue. One day he did not show up. I waited a reasonable length of time, and then rushed to his lodging. Again I smelled the acrid odor of bitter almonds. He lay on his back, his face pale but almost smiling. . . ."

The first time I heard this story I was upset and perplexed. I had not known the luckless man, but I seemed to sense his spirit roaming through the halls at the Station. At first I thought that his life had been all goodness and sacrifice. He had given his life to surgery, and he had even willed his books, instruments, and savings to his hospital. In reviewing this surgeon's life, all seemed fine and grand, worthy of admiration. But the suicide bothered me: it was a miserable end. I remembered his questions: "Why let *me* suffer? Why must I continue to live in torture? What good is it?" Thinking of these cries of anguish, I tried to extenuate his desperate act. But I could not, and the more I thought of it, the finer seemed those who looked death in the face without flinching.

Think of the noble death of Andrea Ferrari, Cardinal Archbishop of Milan. I can still recall, after so many years, how vividly Dr. Michele Meda, my colleague in the surgical pavilion, had described the case. He had performed a tracheotomy on him, for a terrible cancer had invaded the larynx, clogging and closing the respiratory apparatus. Dr. Meda told me that Cardinal Ferrari knew the exact nature of his disease, and he wanted to know the exact truth. He realized that there was no hope, and despite the atrocious pain accompanying the disease, he refused morphine, as he did not wish to cloud his mind during his last days.

True, he had the inestimable comfort of the Faith: he was a saint, as his flock knew. If you visit his tomb in the cathedral, you will find it always covered with roses and violets.

There is no point pretending that all surgeons have such faith and goodness, and are prepared to suffer for the good of their souls, even refusing morphine. But among the doctors who faced diagnosis in the grand manner, I remember a colleague of mine, whose conduct was both exemplary and affecting.

He had been my companion during my first years at the hospital. We had both served in the incurable ward, a veritable anteroom of hell where fetid gangrene, cancer, and ulcer cases, all beyond hope, waited for death. He was older than I, and was already an assistant, while I was scarcely an interne. I helped him, every morning, to make dressings, though the stench was so bad that I thought it might be fine to lose my sense of smell. He attended these poor creatures with the utmost tenderness, washing, disinfecting, deluding, and comforting them. He even joked with some of them.

When our daily stint was over, and we left this inferno, he rubbed his hands together, and lighted a good Virginia cigar to disinfect (he claimed) his breathing apparatus.

"What do you think of those patients of ours? I think I know a cure for them. . . ."

"What do you mean?"

"A lead cure."

"Which means? . . ."

"Just that—a good dose of lead: lead bullets fired by a revolver." He laughed good-naturedly.

He was attached to another ward, and I lost track of him for a long time. I knew that he had made a name for himself in various clinics. He married, and had two children. His friends thought a happy marriage had been the final crown of his career. But about thirty years or so later, chance brought us together. One morning he strode into my laboratory. I was about to greet him warmly, when I realized this was not a social call.

"Look at this wart, Majocchi, between my tongue and jaw. I've had it for some time. I've even stopped smoking, but it does not go away. . . . It bothers me."

I put my finger in his mouth, and shuddered. At the back, to the left, on the wall of the buccal cavity, between the base of the tongue and the dental arch, was a hard place extending toward the pharynx. How could I lie? How could I deceive him? I felt confused. I went into the next room to wash my hands, and remained there as long as possible. When I rejoined him, I was somewhat more collected, and I had invented a lie to gain time. I pretended that I was not sure about the diagnosis. I asked for a blood test. He seemed quite put out.

"But I have never had syphilis, Majocchi. I have two strong and healthy children. However, if you wish, take a blood test."

Several days passed, and my anxiety would give me no

rest. I kept asking myself: what can I do for him? Operate? That was impossible: the cancer extended from the back of the mouth to the pharynx and jaw. An operation meant death. I had to try some other method, possibly radium. But how could I deceive him in that case? I decided to consult my radiologist.

"My friend," I said, "our colleague has a cancer of the mouth—an accursed epithelioma that has settled already, and spread. The case is beyond me, do you understand?"

The radiologist was silent. When he spoke, it was in a very small voice: "Listen, Majocchi, we are used to these tragedies. When you surgeons have finished, we come in. Now, we don't like that—to come so late is tantamount to throwing discredit on actinotherapy. In any event, we must do something, at least in a moral sense. On the other hand, I have had occasional good results with epithelioma of the buccal wall—or at least palliatives. Bring me the poor fellow, and I will do all I can. We may be able to do something. . . ."

"Thanks. But meanwhile, what shall I tell him? I fear that he knows the diagnosis, do you understand?"

"Yes, you are right. So many others have ended the same way. These physicians! . . . These diagnoses! . . ." He thought a moment. "We'll have to lie, that's all. I will say it is an inflammation. No, that's no good—inflammation without fever and pain. . . . I have it: a very rare form: actinomycosis or sporotrichosis. What do you think? . . ."

I breathed a sigh of relief. "Very well, but," I added timidly, "actinomycosis is easily cured by radium. But it does not swell the glands . . . cancer does."

"A detail. Let's hope our patient has forgotten *that*. On the other hand, there is none so blind as he who does not wish to see. He will deceive himself, and in the meantime we may find ways and means."

We were agreed. The next day I brought my unlucky confrere, and we explained the plan of treatment to him. He was pale and serious, but he did not object to the idea. He took our advice, and the treatment began. I turned him over to the radiologist and his aides and disappeared for a time from the scene, although I kept myself informed. As a surgeon I was powerless, and I hadn't the courage to go to see the patient.

For some time my poor friend seemed reassured and tranquil. He took his treatments, and went about his daily life as though nothing were the matter. After several weeks, the swelling seemed to diminish. I even began to suspect that I had made a mistake in my diagnosis. The radiologist, however, shook his head. Two months later the glands in the neck began to swell. The radiologist suspended the treatments, and advised an operation to remove the glands. The patient hesitated, asked time to think it over, and then decided against an operation.

The radiotherapy was continued intermittently for several months, and the results were not wholly negligible. But one evening the patient's wife phoned to ask my advice. Her husband remained calm and carefree, but she was anxious about his swollen glands. The sick man reassured her and the children, too, by his persistent calm. Nevertheless, he was undoubtedly in pain, for some nights he sat bolt upright in bed, as though afflicted by a terrible nightmare. I did not know what to say to her. I guessed that the catastrophe was at hand. In spite of our efforts, the true diagnosis was bound to come out.

Events moved quickly. The cancer ulcerated, and a hor-

rible odor came from his mouth: the patient was racked
by pain, and had to resort to morphine. The cachexy was
more serious, and his strength dwindled. He had even given
up his work, for he could not get up. And yet he remained
confident, encouraging and comforting his family.

One day I received an urgent phone call from his wife.
She asked me to hurry, as her husband wished to see me
before night. I went, but at the door of the sickroom my
heart began to fail me. As soon as I opened the door, I was
smothered by the infectious and well-known odor of the
old incurable ward—the anteroom of death.

My beloved colleague lay back on the pillows. He was
unrecognizable: the throat was monstrously swollen, and
the face was cadaverous. He opened his eyes, summoned up
a feeble smile, and signed for his wife to leave us together.
After painfully getting his breath, he began very softly,
almost sighing:

"Pardon me, if I have disturbed you . . . but I do not
want to die without thanking you for what you have done
for me. You did everything you could, my poor old friend,
to delude and deceive me, out of sheer kindness of heart.
But you could not succeed. I had diagnosed the thing, at
the very start. . . ."

He had to stop for shortness of breath.

"You wanted me to believe in actinomycosis . . . But
since when has actinomycosis caused the glands to swell in
this fashion?"

I shuddered, and a cold sweat moistened my brow. I had
a horrible thought: this man had concealed his own knowledge of his illness. He knew that he was doomed, and had
said nothing to anyone. For all these long months he had

never betrayed himself. It was incredible: more, it was sublime.

"Yes," he resumed, "I diagnosed my case, and I was tempted to end it all. Do you remember the incurable ward, Majocchi, and the way we joked about the lead cure? I was tempted . . . I still am. But I have won through. It reflects no credit on me—I am thinking of my poor children. What would console them if I killed myself?"

He stopped a moment. The thought of his children had moved him: tears glistened on his sallow and wasted cheeks. As for myself, I was on the point of bursting into tears— the torture was wearing me out.

"One last thing," he continued. "I do not know how to say it. But listen, Majocchi, we have had our happy times together, and we have said plenty of foolish things. But tell me, do you think that everything stops now? Think, think well. . . . When a person is about to die, things assume a different aspect. . . . Now, please give me the usual injection."

I rose, washed, and took the syringe. I made a supreme effort, and injected that tiny centigram of morphine that gave him relief for some hours.

He dozed off slowly, and when I saw that he was asleep, I rose, and tiptoed over to the bed. Then I kissed him very gently on his poor ravaged face which had once looked so happy . . . and then I rushed out.

When I was in the dark street, my calm deserted me. . . . I burst into bitter tears which tore my heartstrings, and in these tears were all the pain, all the bitterness, all the agony of the surgeon's life.

Chapter XXI

MELANCHOLY

Quando malinconia
Batte del cor la porta.
—Carducci

THE SURGEON IS SUPPOSED TO BE HEARTLESS AND IRRELIGIOUS. The public pictures him in operating gear, with his rubber apron, more or less bloody rubber gloves, and, in his hands, the terrifying instruments: bistoury, saw, pliers, forceps . . . the arsenal of torture. A butcher, in short, who cannot be sensitive because force of habit has made him indifferent to the pain of others. A materialist, because he gives himself over to the study of corporeal phenomena, and treats them with mechanical means. He is a skeptic by mental discipline, and a cynic by necessity.

This public opinion is no doubt exaggerated. Possibly it is partly hereditary, transmitted by many generations of ancestors, and going back to the time when the surgeon was really a butcher, when he operated without the help of anesthesia, and when his activity manifested itself in apparently brutal and savage acts. But the surgeon of today bears no resemblance to his ancestors, and does not deserve his notoriety.

The surgeon's business is to cure, if he can, and cut the organs and intestines only as a last resort. It is natural for him to evolve a special psychology, since he tends to consider only the material of which the members are composed. His studies and profession incline him to reasoning somewhat like this:

"Life is merely a resultant of the physical and chemical properties of the substance out of which are formed the tissues and the cellular elements. Just as hydrogen and oxygen unite chemically to form water, and in combining release a certain sum of energy, so in the formation of the tissues, in the depths of the cellular protoplasm, one finds infinitely complex chemical reactions, many physical phenomena whence comes that resultant of energy known as life. Life is nothing more than the resultant of a combination of chemical reactions and physical phenomena. It manifests itself as much as the substances making up the human body allow; it is exhausted and disappears when the reagents are exhausted. This is death."

So the surgeon tends to consider the vital function as an explanation of natural phenomena, and his activity is usual in as far as he restores to the human organs the conditions changed by a disease or traumatic lesion. In short, the surgeon is accustomed to think of himself as a mechanic. He is to the human body what the engineer is to the machine.

The engineer fixes and strengthens the spokes of a wheel that is broken; the surgeon brings together the pieces of a broken bone, and he keeps them together by means of apparatus—if necessary, he joins them together with sutures. Thus he re-establishes the continuity of the bone, so that it may resume its function of support and motion. If the health of a vital organ is endangered by, let us say, bad circulation, the surgeon endeavors to remove the obstacles and restore to the organ the best nutritive conditions.

Take a common example. A portion of the intestine

springs from its natural abdominal cavity, and lodges in a hernial sac. The neck of the sac, or rather the base of the hernia, leans on the intestine, and hinders the circulation. The blood no longer arrives freely in the intestinal loop, and no longer carries to the organ those nutritive materials necessary to its life. Such are strangulated hernia and ruptured intestine: doomed themselves, they may bring death to the entire organism.

But the surgeon intervenes. He raises the strangling band, and allows the blood to irrigate properly the tissues otherwise doomed to gangrene and death. The organ is reborn under his hands: he brings about the resumption of those nutritive conditions, of those physical and chemical phenomena that constitute the very essence of life.

Not only do these physical and chemical phenomena explain life, but also the most delicate functions as well: gastrointestinal digestion is nothing more than a totality of certain movements (peristaltic, antiperistaltic, etc.) and of chemical reactions to which are essential the reagents secreted by the organism itself (hydrochloric acid, pepsin, etc.). The same is true of the respiration, circulation, and all other functions.

The surgeon is wont to consider the organ dead as soon as the sum of the conditions necessary for its functioning no longer exists. The physiologist, on the other hand, can keep certain parts of the organism alive by producing artificial conditions that resemble the natural one. We know that life can be maintained in the head of a decapitated dog by injecting blood in the carotid (Brown-Sequard), and that the glycogenic function can be maintained in a liver separated from its host (Claude Bernard). When I was at the Rockefeller Institute I saw some of the amazing things done by Carrel, who amputated ears, kidneys, and limbs of animals, kept them in special liquids for a while, and then, after a while, grafted them on other animals, and there they continued to live.

The surgeon is used to seeing altered or endangered not only organic functions, but also those of the nervous system, which because of its delicacy sometimes seems outside the material field entirely.

I came across the most astonishing facts during the war. I have already spoken of the soldier who, after being wounded in the frontoparietal region, lost his speech, with the exception of a single word: the name of his native village. Those wounded in the occipital region lost their sight completely, though the eyes remained perfectly intact. There have been many remarkable cases of individuals who, after being knocked on the head, forget well-known facts, even a whole language, and, at times, completely lose their memories. Sometimes these faculties return after other traumata or surgical operations.

Epilepsy often follows a blow on the head, and traumata can change character and conduct. Brave soldiers, good fathers, gay and carefree companions—all may, after a blow on the head, become unbalanced, violent, irresolute, criminal. After a certain surgical operation not only have I cured epilepsy, but I have also improved the patient's character.

Even more troublesome are the moral changes that can be traced to certain alterations of the glands of internal secretion and the endocrine glands. Even in remote antiquity changes in character due to removal of the testicles were commented upon, particularly if these accidents happened at the time of puberty. But gynecologists are still more familiar with the mental disturbances caused by the removal of the ovaries. An increase in the secretion of the thyroid gland (hyperthyroidism) notably modifies the character, while the surgeon who operates on the neck knows that its reduction or, even worse, its removal, leads to degeneration of the mind and of the will (strumiprivic cachexy and cretinism).

Needless to say, the surgeon who constantly sees such phenomena, and familiarizes himself with their various manifestations, arrives insensibly at the belief that life and, consequently, soul and mind are only an emanation of matter, and that without matter, that is, without our living body, there could be no question of the survival of the soul. If, outside of his practice, the surgeon devotes himself to research, he becomes even more convinced. Experimenting on dogs, as is the custom, uncovers many analogies in anatomical structure, many resemblances in the functions, and some investigators tend to draw conclusions (rather too sweeping) based on these analogies between human and canine life.

If one asks the surgeon with such an orientation about the immortality of the soul, he springs a counterquestion at once: how about animals? Surgeons, especially the young ones, are apt to dismiss the most profound metaphysical problems with a laugh. It is quite true that surgical science and operative practice are not likely to make the mind receptive to metaphysical thought.

Far from it!

Very well. However, I have seen some odd changes in my time.

I have known very able surgeons, true scientists, who after being materialists most of their lives, became believers during their last few years. I do not know precisely what ideas Edoardo Porro held in his youth, but it is certain that the will and testament of this celebrated obstetrician and gynecologist is a monument to faith, to the immortality of soul, and to a belief in God.

Certain passages in this document are very interesting: "Never," he wrote, "was my belief in God lessened during my decline in life: the thought of a future life has always been present in my mind. Those who pretend that science is destined to materialism are either mistaken, or want to be mistaken."

I long followed very closely the career of my first and very famous teacher, Luigi Mangiagalli, and I remained on such friendly terms with him that he told me his intimate scientific and moral convictions. I still recall the discussions I had with him while we were walking on the heights of Premeno. The peace of the countryside, where he was not weighed down by his many duties, made him more accessible and affable. At that time (1905), the great surgeon was an undeviating scientific materialist. But when he died —it was quite sudden—I heard that in his last moments he had asked for a priest. It seemed incredible in view of his past history, but I asked Dr. Pezzi, who was with him at the end, about it: it was absolutely true.

Another famous teacher also changed his spiritual beliefs during the war. I mean Attilio Rossi, a master of gynecology and obstetrics. I have already spoken at some length about this remarkably intelligent and philanthropic man. I was Ferri's close friend, the recipient of his most intimate confidences. We had many long discussions about biology, physiology, and metaphysics, during which he maintained his materialistic convictions. He did not believe in the immortality of the soul; he did not believe in a future life. But during his last years, he gradually modified his views, and on the eve of his death turned to the consolations of religion.

My friend Baldo Rossi, the famous rector of the University of Milan, after a very active and celebrated career, wished "to die in the faith of my mother." And many more of my colleagues evolved in just the same way.

Was it fear? Weakness? Senility? Admittedly one of these reasons, in some cases, but not in all.

Dr. Porro was not weak in the head when he wrote his last convincing words, for he was still young and in full possession of his faculties. Senator Mangiagalli certainly had his wits about him the day he was stricken, for at two o'clock he had proposed a toast of amazing lucidity at the Rotary Club at Milan. As for Professor Baldo Rossi, he had attended, only a few days before his death, a medical congress at Bari, where he had been vigorous in discussion, and had been assigned a subject to present at the congress the following year.

There was nothing senile about these men.

Possibly it was fear.

But I cannot admit that the men I named were craven and mean-spirited. They never were, and they never could have been.

I think I have a better explanation. As soon as one gets older he evolves a psychological set-up that permits him to see things from another point of view.

And in the surgeon's life and mind there are very powerful sources of faith. First of all, the surgeon lives, and passes his whole life, among the sick. Their unhappiness surrounds him, torments him, haunts him unceasingly.

"You are used to the pain of others," our patients say. Apparently, but not really.

"*Cirusicus immisericors esse debet,*" the ancients said: that is, the surgeon must gird himself against the pain of others; he must harden his heart if he is to go ahead with his work without wavering, without being upset, without hesitating. He has to be strong lest his wrist tremble, cold lest his feelings overwhelm him, and calm and serene lest he forget the direction he must take, the program he must follow.

But when the operation is over, the mask falls. He becomes a man of feeling, for his heart beats, and he suffers . . . like the rest of the world. When a disease is beyond his resources, when he is compelled to look on irremediable suffering . . . then too he feels anguish and unspeakable torture.

Irremediable suffering, incurable disease! . . . Here are whole wards full of patients with tubercular bones—diseases which seem to take a savage delight in gnawing at one bone after another the whole life through. Here are those afflicted by Pott's disease, whose cold abscesses run from the vertebrae toward the pelvis and loins, while the vertebrae themselves are crushed, bending the backbone, pressing against the spinal nerves, and causing paresis, paralysis, and, very often, excruciating pain. Then there are the cancer institutes and their sufferers. Cancer of the thorax, obstinate, constantly reappearing tumors on the breast, ravaged tongues and jaws—and the poor victims beyond the powers of X-ray or radium! . . .

But the worst of all are the diseases (chronic, more especially) of the nervous system. They keep neurological institutes and asylums filled to overflowing.

The surgeon passes his days amid this pain and suffering, and so comes to the conclusion that there is more evil than good in life, more pain than joy, and more agony than solace. It is no wonder that he sometimes asks:

"Why is there so much pain and misery in the world? What is the good of it all?"

Chapter XXII

EPILOGUE

e giunta sul pendìo
precipita l'età. . . .
—Parini

WELL, I HAVE FINISHED.

I have finished writing my memoirs, and meanwhile my surgical career nears the meridian, and then . . . decline.

Decline! It is a sad word, but one must accept it.

When I think of it, I can't believe it. It seems only yesterday that I took my degree, and besides, I feel that physically I am the same man I was thirty years ago: the same energy, the same mental agility, the same health.

It is true that the mirror shows me a few gray hairs and wrinkles. Also, after a hard day operating, I sometimes feel tired and spent—I could stand a bit of rest. I feel like a traveler who has taken a long journey. But give me a few days' vacation, and I am as happy and healthy as ever, more eager than ever to get to work.

But how long can I continue this life of strife and abnegation?

Mangiagalli, when he was fifty years old, had a way of repeating, "Sixty, yes, sixty." By that he meant to indicate that he was *irrevocably* determined to retire at that age. But when he was past sixty, he said seventy. When he was seventy he was amazed at being pensioned, though it didn't seem quite right to give up his classes. When he died, at the age of seventy-eight, he was actually at the height of his professional activity. He had a sudden heart attack one afternoon, though that very morning he had operated in his private hospital.

Some years ago I said jokingly to my assistants that I would retire when I could no longer draw the finest silk through the eye of the intestinal needle. Well, I am still threading my needles with the greatest of ease—without spectacles, you understand.

And besides, if I retired, what would I do?

Would it be right, in the fulness of my physical powers, to refuse to work, for the sake of rest and idleness? It may be true that the surgeon's daring wanes with age, but it is equally true that experience increases just as much. My surgical successes wax with the years. I save many now I would once have lost, and I owe countless little operative ideas to my daily work.

The day will come, however, when all these accumulated treasures will have to yield to the decay of the senses and the weakness of old age. But I hope that day is far off.

What a godsend work is to the man who is growing old!

It is pastime, pleasure, satisfaction, reason for existence. When I treat, study, and operate on my patients, I become young again, I forget my cares—I taste the joys of life. But when there is no work, I feel sad and bored. A thousand dismal thoughts come into my head, and there is a cloud of gloom around me. It is the sadness of the man who has traveled a long, hard road, climbed a steep mountain, left bits of his skin at the cross roads, lost many of his illusions.

Sometimes, in an idle moment, I look back on the long,

hard road, and I feel a nostalgia for those distant years. Strange visions, insignificant facts, unimportant, futile details I had long forgotten—all assail my memory. How I studied and worked! And how much envy, ill feeling, and actual hostility I had to overcome! How I had to battle for my place in life! Well, all this strife took so much time that I have arrived at the height of my career without knowing it.

And now?

Now that I have fought my battle, and won it, I have only to await the economic end: my pension. And the physiological end: death.

Death.

The icy thought often assails me. Naturally. My work lies very largely in hospitals and nursing homes.

And how can I forget death when my friends, colleagues, and students are picked off by the years?

Hasn't Casnigo, the beloved clown, the hero of our student dinners, he who drank to happiness and youth, gone forever? Besta went, and then Sacconighi, and many others who had shared the hopes and joys of my university days.

The specter of death trails me, haunts me. I exorcise it with work, but it comes back when I am idle.

But who does not think of death? "I have not a thought that death has not molded," Michelangelo wrote to Vasari, and Axel Munthe, quoting the words, says that they actually frighten him.

The most pessimistic of authors, those who have cursed life and invoked death as the sole liberator, were almost *scared* to death when they came within its reach. Leopardi fled from Naples to escape cholera. Bordeaux and the plague could not hold Montaigne. And Schopenhauer, after writing many books to prove that life was evil and death the sole good, would not even let death be spoken of in his presence.

But death is the doctor's personal enemy. All our work is directed to combating it, averting it, snatching some victim away from its clutches. And the very fact that I have spent my days in the constant, desperate battle brings up another question: what is the aim of life? Why so many battles, why so much suffering? What end does man's never-ending efforts serve? And not only man's, but the whole human species', the universe's?

That is a question!

Tormenting and fraught with difficulties, it is equally puzzling to surgeons, physicians, and biologists. It haunted me while I was studying philosophy. All my life I have thought of it, but in vain.

It may be said that man works for economic progress, social perfection, and a thoroughly beneficent political state. It may be that the human species will, after infinite modifications and improvements, produce the perfect individual: the *superman*. But even the superman, flawless in body and mind and living in a perfect social and economic atmosphere, must die. No human power can give him immortality.

Well, what *is* the aim of life?

In the midst of this confusing labyrinth, in this painful search for the truth, a delicious memory persists, and gives me peace.

I was still a small child, sitting at my mother's knee, when

I asked her: "Mamma dear, why were we brought into the world?" I still seem to hear her inspired words: "God brought us here to know Him, to love Him, and to serve Him in this life, that we may enjoy Him in another world."

It seems to me that this is the Word, the solution, the oracle that comprehends all the wisdom of the universe.

Now I understand why my friend Baldo Rossi, the renowned Rector of the University of Milan, after sixty years of study, research, and hard work, wished to return to the faith of his mother, a simple countrywoman. And Fradeletto, after a life devoted exclusively to intellectual and moral peregrinations, ended his noble existence with the words: "Let us return to Christ!"

At last I understand why Jesus preferred the lowly, the gentle, and the poor in spirit.

"Pleni sunt coeli et terra gloria tua!" cries the ascetic in an ecstasy, and the surgeon can well pronounce the same words when, seeking for the divine craftsmanship, he finds it in the admirable fabric of the human body, in the perfection of its limbs, organs, tissues. There is so much science in it all that no biologist can ever understand or know it. . . .

So it is easy to know God and to love Him: it is much more difficult to serve Him. For if each of us, having arrived at a mature age, looks back on the work he has done, he feels discouraged. None has served God as he should have done—we can only think of the mistakes we've made.

As I look back on my surgical work, I find that I often could have done better. . . .

So?

During my last years of activity I must multiply my

good deeds, and when I arrive at the goal I will still have the same overwhelming hope: to enjoy God in the next world. My dying prayer shall be the words that I had engraved on my mother's tomb:

In te, Domine, speravi, non confundar in aeternum!